Foreword

I'm always delighted to see books like this one getting into print because they do so much to inspire new keepers; developing enthusiasm and heightening interest in this wonderful hobby.

Keeping chickens at home ticks all the right boxes. It is a wonderful activity to be involved with, especially if you have young children who can be encouraged take part. In an age that's increasingly dominated by Facebook, games consoles and text messaging, prising your youngsters away from their screens and out into the fresh air is becoming ever harder. But throw a cute chicken or two into the equation, plus the prospect of collecting warm eggs from the nest box every morning, and it's amazing how quickly this sedentary behaviour can be changed!

But this fascination isn't limited to the young; the young at heart can benefit too. Anyone can quickly find themselves hooked on keeping poultry; it is the nature of the hobby. It really can turn out to be thoroughly addictive, and many keepers follow a predictable path as their passion develops. Typically, most start with just two or three hybrid hens, simply intended to supply delicious, healthy, fresh eggs. But things soon progress from there. Joining a local poultry club, or starting to read a specialist magazine like Practical Poultry, introduces the budding keeper to the fascinating world of the pure breed.

With 100 or so distinct breeds of domesticated chicken to choose from – a good number of which are in desperate need of conservation support nowadays – new keepers truly are spoilt for choice. The variety of size, shape, plumage colour and pattern ensures that there's something to suit all tastes, and it's never too long before hybrid keepers start hankering after a pure breed or two for added interest. Then, of course, there's the temptation of breeding. On the face of it, it's simplicity itself, and few can resist the prospect of producing fluffy little chicks from hatching eggs in just three weeks flat!

However, it's vital to appreciate that success with poultry – whatever your level – involves careful and organised management. Chickens will only thrive if the conditions in which they are living are right. They are extremely sensitive to their environment, with issues such as available space, housing, feeding and inter-flock relationships all being of fundamental importance. That's where a book like this can really prove its worth. Being packed with essential, practical information about looking after chickens in the back garden environment, it offers the novice keeper a valuable insight into what's required to help keep their birds both healthy and happy. Staying on top of predator, rodent and parasite control are other key requirements, as is developing the ability to recognise when a bird's health is suffering.

While keeping poultry is hardly rocket science, there's certainly a bit more to it than many people first imagine. So it's important to learn all you can from books such as this one, so that your birds remain a constant and productive pleasure for years to come.

Chris Graham

Editor, Practical Poultry Magazine

Contents

4

Introduction

Chicken Keeping is a joy. You will have a constant supply of the most yummy eggs you have ever had and the fun of watching your hen's personalities develop as they go about their day, chatting to each other whilst looking for tasty morsels in the ground I want to encourage every one who is considering keeping a few chickens in the garden to take the plunge and go for it.

You will be amazed at how friendly and tame the chickens become and how much fun they are to have around. I originally wrote this book to accompany the Chicken Keeper courses I run, but it has now grown to a point where it has become a book in its own right and I hope it will both inspire you to order your hen house now and reassure you that you will be able to cope with all eventualities in this most rewarding of hobbies.

The Breeds of chicken section is restricted to the readily available hybrids and a few traditional breeds. The reasons for this are simple. This book is aimed at the beginner who wants to keep a few chickens for the wonderful eggs they produce. The hybrids are bred specifically to be highly productive hens, producing good quality eggs. There is a cost element in feeding and looking after chickens, so I believe it is most cost effective to feed a chicken which is going to produce an average of 280 eggs a year. Indeed, it costs the same to feed a traditional breed hen who may lay less than 200 eggs a year. Hybrids also have the advantage of being good looking chickens and will soon become tame and friendly, so I can't think of any better hens to start with. They do, however, mainly only lay brown eggs, so if you want a range of egg colours you can, later on, branch out into the world of the traditional hen, of which there are many.

The chapter on eggs has been fascinating to research and if anyone knows of any other egg tricks for the Children's section do please pass them on to me. My children had fun making the egg animals and these were used for the accompanying photos in this book. Let your children's imagination run riot and I am sure they will have as much fun as mine did.

As the introduction to the Troubleshooting section states, the list of possible ailments is in no way intended to put you off. Quite the contrary, it is designed to give you the confidence to buy your first two or three chickens safe in the knowledge that you are equipped to deal with any difficulties you may encounter. The troubleshooting section is almost entirely based on research, as I have not come across most of the diseases and problems listed. I have had one case of Scaley Leg, which was soon dealt with and I am able to cope with the inevitable outbreak of red mite. If you have the misfortune to encounter something not covered in the troubleshooting section, then please contact me at **alison@chickenkeeper.co.uk** and I will research your query.

Whatever reason you have for wanting to keep chickens, this book comes with a warning:

Chickens are Addictive!

Practising the application of louse powder

1

Preparation for Your New Hobby

This chapter discusses the choices and decisions to be made at the outset of starting down the path of Chicken Keeping. Why do you want to keep hens and what are the main hurdles to be overcome before starting?

Points To Consider

It is worth taking a little time at the outset to plan where the chickens are to go in the garden, and how they are to be housed. Even before that, it is advisable to check that your house deeds do not prevent you from keeping chickens. If your title deeds do not allow you to keep chickens, amongst other animals, on the premises, it is a civil matter. This means that the covenant is enforceable by any person who is legally entitled to enjoy the benefit of the covenant and who owns land within the vicinity of your house. The whole legal area of enforcement of a covenant is complicated and a neighbour would have to go to the lengths of applying to a Court for an injunction to stop you keeping your couple of hens.

There are two main neighbour objections to hens next door: a cockerel and 'hens attract rats'. Hens come into lay naturally and do not need a cockerel around bossing them about and thrusting his unwanted attentions on them. A cockerel will take to bragging about his prowess at dawn and even earlier; a sure way of annoying the neighbours. Once your neighbours are assured that

you are not intending to keep a cockerel they should feel more reassured. A hen will often 'announce' that she has laid an egg, but this only lasts a few minutes. For the rest of the time they are quiet or gently 'bouk, bouk' to each other as they go about their day. Just to finish the bit on cockerels, they are often bad tempered and aggressive. The odd one can be friendly and good company, but you won't know until you've had him a while and it is very difficult to re-house a cockerel. If you buy fertile eggs, or day old chicks of a non-sex-link variety, there will be a percentage of boys which hatch. The agreement with the supplier is usually that they will take the boy chicks back.

The myth that chickens attract rats also has to be dealt with. It is not the chickens; it is the food which attracts rats. So long as you keep the food area clean of spillages and tip any left over food at night back into the secure food bin, there is no attraction to rats or mice. Indeed, the average compost heap has a much bigger attraction to rats as they love the consistency and warmth of the centre of a compost heap. If there are rats in your garden you have a legal responsibility to get rid of them.

Also, do you have an available chicken sitter? (At Hook Farm we have chicken boarding facilities, but that may not be available in your area.) Will the neighbour who feeds the cat and waters the plants also remember to feed the chickens and shut them in at night? There is always the incentive of keeping the eggs they find, but holidays are something to consider.

Next is the decision on which hens to get and how many of them. The two criteria are related because three hybrid hens will supply the average family with all the eggs they need and a few to give to family and friends besides. Three pure bred hens will still have you buying eggs in your weekly shop, as each one may only lay an egg a week.

There are many reasons to keep a few hens. If you simply want entertaining pets with the benefit of an egg from time to time, then browse through some chicken breed books and choose a breed that catches your eye. Do a little research on your chosen breed as they are not all suitable as garden pets.

Some can be aggressive as a breed and other can be too nervous, but there will be one to suit you. Even better, pick a few breeds and have one of each. They will be a big talking point at a summer barbecue with friends in the garden!

There are an increasing number of hybrids available, which can lay an average of 280/300 eggs a year. Chicken customers often comment with surprise how pretty the Black Rocks and Speckledies are when they come up the garden to see them. There seems to be a concept that all prolific egg laying hens will look like battery chickens (who are also quite pretty), which is far from the truth. If you want to keep hens for the eggs, with the benefit of being pretty as well, then it will be best to choose from the range of hybrids.

Having decided on a breed or breeds, the question of how many to keep will have been answered. I have often had customers come to buy 6 Black Rocks, but rapidly change their minds to 2 or 3 when I ask what they are going to do with 6 eggs a day, every day. Alternatively, do consider having 6 hybrids, knowing that you will only need the eggs from 3 of them for your household, with the intention of selling the surplus eggs. It will not take long to build up regular customers and the income is a welcome contribution to the cost of the food. With a bit of luck, your own eggs might be free!

I find that customers who come to look at the hybrids, but have set their heart on a particular pure breed, will return a few months later to buy a couple of hybrids to produce the eggs that they aren't getting with the pure breeds. By the same token, a family with a flock of 4 hybrids wanting to expand, but not wanting more eggs, can choose some 'eye candy' in the shape of some stunning pure breed hens safe in the knowledge that they will not be overrun with eggs.

There really are the right hens out there for you.

2

Definition of a Chicken

Not that I would doubt that you know what a chicken is, but for pure completion of my work I thought it best to provide a definition.

Definition

Kingdom:	Animal
Phyllum:	Vertebrate (with spine)
Branch:	Gnathostomata (with upper and lower jaws)
Class:	Aves (birds)
Sub-Class:	Neornithes (without teeth)
Sub-Division:	Carinatae (with keeled sternum or breastbone)
Order:	Gallinae (terrestrial birds, short wings legs & toes for running & scratching)
Genus:	Gallus (cock-like birds)
Species:	Gallus Domesticus (breeding in domestic conditions)

Dictionary of Terms

Chick:	Young bird (male or female) up to the age of 6 weeks
Pullet:	Female in the first laying season
Point-of-Lay Pullet:	Young female 15-21 weeks which will shortly come into lay
Hen:	Female which has completed one season of laying
Cockerel:	Male bird up to the age of one year
Cock:	Male bird over the age of one year
Chicken:	Originally a term for a male or female up to the age of one year, but now also a general term for all ages.
Dubbing:	Dubbing is the practice of removing the comb and wattles. It was done to chicks which were bred for cock fighting to minimise damage in a fight. The combs and wattles are full of blood capillaries and damage in a fight would result in a flow of blood, potentially obscuring the bird's eyesight. Dubbing was also used in breeds where the combs and wattles are so big and dangly, such as the Leghorn, that they interfered with the bird's sight and feeding.
Capon:	A male chicken castrated when young to improve the quality of its flesh for food. This was done by inserting a hormone pellet into the comb of the young cockerel. Caponising is illegal in Great Britain.

Combs

Combs have a fleshy consistency and contain many blood capillaries, which gives them their red appearance. Combs may be small, medium or large depending on the breed. Most chickens have a single vertical comb with serrations or spikes pointing up. In some breeds, such as the Leghorn, it flops to one side. The main function of the comb is to help the bird lose heat in hot weather, but it does have other functions as well. Interestingly, the comb is one of the areas of skin, along with the wattles and ears, which is available to sunlight and assists in the production of Vitamin D.

A young pullet will have a small, pink comb which grows and then reddens as she comes into lay. A nice red comb indicates to a cockerel that the hen is laying and ready to produce him strong chicks. If she goes broody, a hen's comb will lose its colour to tell the cockerel that she is out of service for a while and to leave her alone. The same happens during the moult and the hen's comb loses its red colour.

It is interesting that each head and comb combination is unique and a hen can recognize around 50 of her fellow flock members on the basis of head patterns. In winter a coating of Vaseline will help protect especially fleshy combs from frostbite. Combs are a good indication of the health of a hen. A lovely bright red comb indicates a happy, healthy, laying hen. A purple comb can indicate a heart condition.

Feathers

A chick hatches with a soft down all over it. During the next week sheaths appear on the wings and then the feathers push out through the sheaths. The sheaths are like straws that push through the skin first to make a tunnel for the feather to push up through afterwards. Depending on the breed, a chick will have all its first feathers between 4–6 weeks. At between 14–22 weeks a chicken changes its feathers again, this time for its adult ones. The baby wing feathers fall out and the adult ones push through, starting in the middle of the wing. Lastly, the tail feathers grow and when the tail is fully in place the hen will come into lay. The time taken depends

on the breed. The Black Rocks that come to me at 16 weeks have all their adult feathers and come into lay at 18 weeks during the laying season.

Chickens, like all birds, will preen their feathers to look their best. As they run their beaks through the feathers they comb the barbs of the feather back into place. A feather has a central shaft which is bare at the end where it is attached to the skin. Individual barbs grow from the shaft. Each one of these has barbules with a tiny hook on the end. As the hen moves her beak along them it rejoins any, like a zip, that may have come undone. The strength of a

fully zipped feather is amazing, providing wind proofing and the strength for flight in wing feathers. The beak also moves oil from the preening gland at the base of the feather along the feather, making it waterproof. Water birds have more oil in these glands than chickens because waterproofing is vital to them. Chickens have less and are definitely not waterproof! They can look extremely bedraggled in wet weather, especially as they do not seem to seek shelter from the rain. They do not seem to mind being bedraggled and it does not seem to affect their laying rate.

Once a year they will moult their feathers and grow new ones. Some may just lose a few feathers and others even seem to lose most of them. It requires protein to grow new feathers, so the hen diverts her protein use from egg production to feather growth during the moult.

Coming Into Lay

As above, an egg laying chicken will come into lay as soon as she has finished growing all her feathers. It also depends on the amount of daylight in the day, so a hen feathered up in autumn may not come into lay until the days start to get longer in January/February. Her total egg laying capacity is not lost in the meantime; it just means that you have fed her through the winter for no benefit of eggs. As discussed above and in the Health section, she will not lay eggs during her annual moult. Egg laying, or not, is directly linked to the state of feather growth as both processes use valuable minerals and protein. If the hen has to use her resources to make new feathers, she will divert her energies from egg making and concentrate on her feathers.

A hybrid can start laying as early as 18 weeks. Other breeds may start a little later, but on average a hen will be laying by 21 weeks. A young pullet will be recognisable as such by her underdeveloped and pale comb. The Black Rock and Speckledy in the pictures are 16 weeks old. Note that the Speckledy doesn't have her full tail yet. In another 2 weeks their

combs will have grown to full size and will redden up as they start to lay. After that I find it difficult to tell the age of a chicken, so I ring their legs with colour coded plastic rings to denote their age.

When a hen starts laying, the eggs will start off very small, but will get bigger day by day until they are up to the normal size for the breed.

Speckledy

3

Housing

The purchase of a hen house with or without a run is the most expensive aspect of your new hobby. With the increase in popularity in hen keeping has come an explosion of new houses on the market. There is a huge range of houses in a huge range of prices. Many have been designed for looks, with scant regard to practical use and others are perfect as they are, or with a little modification will be even better. This chapter gives the pros and cons for the various options open to you in terms of the housing and run, or pen and will help you decide on the right set up for you.

Which Set Up For You?

So, the decision to keep some hens has been taken. Next, you need to consider how they are to be housed. Can you accommodate a free standing hen house allowing the chickens full run of the garden? Will a free standing house in an enclosed, fenced area of the garden be better? Or is it necessary to restrict the hens to an enclosed run attached to, or under, the hen house? Do you want a choice where the hens can be let out in the garden while you are around, but kept in a run when you are not? How moveable will the hen house and run need to be?

There are a number of houses with attached runs, such as arks, which are intended to be moved around the garden to provide the hens with new pasture. Chickens will scratch every last blade of grass in their area and reduce the ground to bear earth, so there are two options; either move them to new grass or make a plan to cope with the bare earth. If you have a large field or paddock then the option of moving a fixed structure around may work, bearing in mind that you will

be systematically denuding the pasture and creating a patchwork of bare areas. The only reason it will work in a field is because it is not as emotive as systematically destroying your garden in front of your eyes. You can repair the damage by seeding with a chicken compatible ley grass mixture as you move the house and run around, but all that does, in reality, it change the colours of the patchwork pattern as there are batches in various states of re-growth.

Coupled with the systematic destruction of the grass, there is the practical aspect of moving the structure around. Do you have the manpower available to do so regularly?

There are also other practical difficulties to consider with particular reference to arks. They are designed with the intention of permanently housing the hens. As a rule, they have a fairly small footprint and that, indeed, is part of their attraction. However, because of the sloping sides and reducing head height at floor level, the actual area that can be accessed by the hens is much smaller than it looks. Also, when looking at an ark, consider where you are going to put the feeder and drinker. Most arks have removable panels at either end of the underneath run area, but how practical are they for you? Putting the food station at one end seems the obvious answer, but if a feeder gets kicked into the middle, how are you going to retrieve it. Other than finding a small child to send in, you are going to be flat on your belly to reach in and retrieve it.

This next rule applies for whatever housing you are looking at, be it in the flesh as it were, in a magazine, or on the Internet. Consider every aspect of the house, picture it in your garden and imagine yourself on a cold, wet Saturday morning. How are you going to get into it to clean it? What type of access do you have to the house for cleaning and the run for feeding? What access is there to the run? If you have to catch a chicken, collect an egg laid on an odd place or retrieve a kicked over feeder, can you get in to do that?

The Hen House

Whatever circumstances suit you; there are a number of standard criteria for the hen house. If you are buying one, be sure to check the features before you buy. If you are making one, your design should aim to incorporate as many of them as possible.

In no particular order, the standard requirements for a hen house are;

1. There must be a ventilation panel, mesh covered, and situated above the hen's heads. Depending on where the house is sited, it may need to be partially closable against the wind. The droppings give off methane and ethane and ventilation is essential. If there are only a few hens, the gaps under a corrugated roof may suffice, rather than a ventilation panel. Whatever vent is incorporated; it must be above the hens heads. See (3)

2. The house should have sufficient headroom above the chickens on the perch to allow warm air to rise. Damp, musty conditions are to be avoided, as they lead to bronchial conditions.

3. The house has to be draught proof. The hens puff out their soft under-feathers to create a warm air trap between their feather cover and their skin. Much in the same way as a string vest works. If there is a draught it will penetrate the feather cover and the hen will get cold. This will lead to a weakening of the hen and make her more susceptible to disease. Any gaps in the frame below the perch will allow a draught. Remember to check the house regularly as weather wear and tear can lead to draughts.

4. Fencing for the run. A chicken can squeeze through an amazingly small gap, so use chicken mesh and make sure the fence panels fit securely together. Consider wattle hurdles for a more natural look.

5. Make the house door big enough to allow easy cleaning. Cleaning is a large consideration and every little helps. Thick plastic sheeting on the base of the floor, covered in wood shavings or sawdust, will be easy to pull out and clean.

This picture shows two green under perches in place

An 'under perch' under the perches, where droppings are most concentrated will also help.

6. Painting the hen house floor with a wood sealant will help make the floor waterproof and easier to clean out as the surface is smoother.

7. The floor cleaning access should be open at the floor level, so that it is easy to get the floor material out. A front board will make it more difficult to sweep or scoop out.

8. As well as sanitary cleaning, the house also has to be easily kept free of red mite. These little beasts live in any gaps or crevices during the day and come out to feed on the hens at night. Signs and treatment of red mite are dealt with in the troubleshooting section. The more a house can be dismantled, the easier it will be to spray and keep red mite free.

9. Red mite love roof felt and therefore felt is to be avoided. Corrugated roofing is perfect, but don't use the clear one as the hens can be easily frightened by anything suddenly passing over or landing on top. There are polystyrene fillers to fit between the ridges if you want the insulation. Alternatively the ridge gaps can contribute to the ventilation of the house provided it is not situated where the wind will whistle through it.

10. Consider the position and orientation of the house. It may look neatest tucked up against the fence, but in that position it will simply become a stepping stone for the hens to hop on the roof and over the fence. The house should be sited as near to the middle of the pen as possible. Also consider the direction of the prevailing wind and position the house with its back to it, if you can.

11. The chickens will need a perch to sleep on. This makes them feel more comfortable as it is akin to their preferred place of sleeping in a tree. Fixed perches, rather than removable ones, reduce the contact area with the side wall and thus minimise the area available to red mite. The perches should be placed away from the nest boxes and allow a clear area underneath for the hens to move around in. The perches should be rounded on top for extra grip, but not completely round like a broom handle.

12. The house needs feet to keep it off the ground and longer legs if the run is to fit underneath. A house sitting on the ground will start to rot from day one and provides a perfect base for rats, or voles in the case in the picture, to burrow and live happily underneath. This is what we found when

we moved a house which sits on the ground. Also consider wide wheels instead of feet if mobility is a necessary feature.

13. The roof needs to be on a slope either as a straight slope, or an apex. The roof should have at least a 6" overhang to protect the house and especially the ventilation hole. Also consider the direction of the water run off, preferably not directly into the attached run.

14. The position and size of the nest box need to consider both the hen and the egg collection. A hen likes a dark, secluded place to lay eggs. She needs to be able to get into it easily. A board across the front will keep the nesting material in and give her a sense of security. Egg collection needs to be easy, almost child's play, but fox proof.

15. The nest box is usually on the outside, with hen access on the inside. Eggs are collected by lifting the lid, or dropping a hinged front. It need not necessarily be very big as hens will lay in the smallest of places. This area in the picture is the gap between the run of nest boxes and the wall, a width the size of my hand!

16.	Feeding area. Given the British weather, the food containers need to be under cover. The easiest solution is to raise the hen house high enough to allow space to put the food containers underneath. Alternatively, make a weatherproof area for the feeder, such as under a child's plastic table, as I do.

17.	Weight of the hen house. The house should be of a solid construction, with no gaps for draughts to blow in. At the same time, it should be light enough to be easily moved if necessary. The ideal structure is strong, but light.

18.	As well as a large door, a hen house will need a pop hole for daily use of the hens. It needs to be shut at dusk and opened in the morning, to protect against foxes. It can be opened and shut by a sliding door or runners, or by a ramp which is taken up & let down. There are battery operated, automatic pop-hole openers for those who may not be around at dusk, or may not have time in the busy morning.

19.	The pop hole should be the appropriate size for the size of chicken you are keeping. Hens will wait in turn to exit and will come out one by one, albeit at speed. The pop hole needs to be big enough to allow free access, but not too big to allow a fox to get in.

20.	The opening door, or the pop hole, must be able to be secured open. A door which has blown shut will cause mayhem and panic at bedtime as the chickens run to and fro in front of the closed door, not sure what to do next. Instead of simply closing the door on the house at bedtime, you will spend some time searching the pen for your hens who have been forced to find alternative accommodation, often up a tree!

21. If a ramp is needed it must be wide enough for the hens to walk up in comfort, remembering that a hen's legs are either side of her and she can't walk up a narrow ramp by putting her feet one in front of the other, like a gymnast!. It will also need grip bars at it will become very slippery.

22. If egg continuity is a consideration, a poultry house lighting unit may help. It is usually a 12 Volt fluorescent light with a light sensor and microprocessor. This measures the length of daylight and comes on before dawn the next day to keep an overall daylight length of 16 hours. It is designed to be used as the nights draw in during autumn and it can be a good way of ensuring winter eggs. It is, advisable however, to allow the birds peace during the moult, when they should be allowed to moult naturally and have a period of rest and relaxation.

23. In the UK there is no need to heat a hen house as long as it is draught proof. If there are only a few hens they may benefit from some insulation as long as it does not cover up any of the vents. Polystyrene sheets do the trick. If there are a number of hens they will keep each other warm. They can fluff their feathers up, trapping warm air between their skin and the feather surround. It is for this reason that it is important that the hen house is draught proof.

24. You will need to decide what you are going to use on the hen house floor. I find wood shavings to be the best as they are absorbent and do well on the compost heap later. Straw is not good flooring for two reasons. It can remain dry on top and mask the dirt and dampness underneath. All may look fine while the wooden floor is rotting underneath. Also, in muddy conditions at can form a hard ball on the hens' toes, which can be difficult to remove. Straw and mud are, after all, a constituent of wall building in old houses, some of which are still standing today.

Adapt Where Necessary

If a house is perfect for you in most aspects consider adaptations to overcome the shortcomings. For example, if you want an ark but are worried about access to the run, screw hooks in the roof near the entrance to the underneath run and get hanging feeders and drinkers. This will keep them fully accessible. If you like a house that sits on the ground, make it a table to sit on. This will stop the ground rot problem and provide shelter for the hens when needed. If access to the house is limited for cleaning make yourself a new big door in the back or side of the house.

The hen house is by far the most expensive investment for your new hobby. There is a wide choice of house on the market in both design and price. Make a paper or mental tick list of firstly the essential aspects and then those most affecting your set up. Find the house that best suits the criteria and then consider adapting those that aren't quite right for you. Don't reject a house out of hand that may work well with a little adaptation.

Cleaning The Hen House

This is a little like 'how long is a piece of string?' There is a range of tactics to employ to minimise cleaning out time and expense, culminating in the employment of a Saturday boy, as I do! A small flock of 3 to 4 hens will not need cleaning out more than once a week. Having an under perch that can be rinsed

off as necessary will protect the wood shavings underneath and may mean weeks of use for the wood shavings.

Most of the poo done at night is the nice brown solid sort and the brave can use a rubber glove to 'poo pick' the droppings out each day. This will also make the wood shavings last longer. People with horses seem to take to this better than others.

Alternatively, try the deep fill system. The week starts with a thin layer of wood shavings and further layers are put on as necessary to cover the droppings. At the end of the week the whole lot is cleared out and the first thin layer put in to start again.

Putting a thick layer of plastic on the wooden floor before the wood shavings will make removing the soiled wood shavings easier. Maybe use a piece of cardboard and then everything, cardboard and all, can be put on the compost heap.

If you don't use a removable floor protector, then a good flat based hand shovel and bucket, I find the soft plastic ones best, will be your standard equipment. As suggested above, a wood sealant painted on the floor when the house is new will make cleaning out easier. It will also help with preserving the house longer.

Whatever system you use, the house should be fully emptied and cleaned once a month. This will prevent any long term infestations, such as maggots which can live undetected under visibly dry shavings but which are wet underneath, and allow inspection for the dreaded Red Mite.

Reluctance To Go Into The House

Chickens become very attached to their hen house once they are imprinted and can become very frantic if access is denied due to the pop-hole sliding shut or the door being blown closed. Any sign of reluctance to enter the hen house therefore indicates a problem. The obvious one is the existence of red mite and that is the first thing to check. If not that, it could be that the house is too hot and humid. Increasing the ventilation, especially in summer, and decreasing cleaning intervals will solve the problem.

Consider A Spare Temporary House

A temporary house will have a number of practical uses. It does not have to be as well built as the main hen house as it will only house 1, maybe 2, hens at a time, but it must still be practical and draught proof. A chicken feeling under the weather will appreciate a little time out to regroup herself. A spare house is also useful for separating a bullied hen for a while and, indeed, separating the bully to take her down a peg or two. The introduction of new chickens, minimum 2, to an established flock will be easier if the new ones can be housed in the temporary house before being introduced fully. A broody hen can cause havoc in the nest boxes by hogging the favourite nest box and unsettling the others. A few days in the temporary house (sin bin) usually changes her mind about feeling broody.

In all cases for the use of a temporary house, it should be kept in sight of the main pen and where both sets of hens can see each other. This helps with the introduction of new hens as they won't be complete strangers when they do eventually join their new sisters. It also helps hens who have been taken out to remain part of the flock, albeit at a distance. There will then be less chance of aggravation when they are re-introduced.

Keep an eye out for a second hand rabbit or guinea pig cage, as these are ideal as a spare, temporary house.

The Run

Once the decision has been taken to allocate the hens a permanent location, thought and planning will need to go into constructing the pen. The hens will appreciate a range of environments in the pen. They will need access to sunshine, so take out some of the canopy if the area is under a big tree. They will also need shade, so plant a bush, raise the house to give access underneath or recycle an old garden parasol if there is no natural shade. Allow a 'wild' area of an old log, or pile of twigs which will attract bugs and give the hens something to stand on. They like being at different heights and will much appreciate a free standing perch to sit on when they feel like it.

Hens enjoy interest at different heights, so where a treat of corn is thrown on the floor and their food and drink are slightly raised off the ground (see Siting the Food Station in the Feeding chapter) give them interest at head height by hanging old CDs off the perch or a tree and hanging greens up for them to peck at.

Fencing

If the hens have the full run of the garden little continuous care is needed. Initially, the boundaries will need to be escape proof, remembering that a chicken can squeeze through a remarkably small gap, or, in the case of a bantam, even smaller. The disadvantage with allowing free reign of the garden is that chicken poo will be distributed randomly and fully all over the garden. If this is an issue, then allocating a fixed area to the chickens will be best. Whether fencing

the garden perimeter, or the area of a fixed pen, high fencing or fencing with no foothold will be helpful in keeping out the foxes. Foxes belong to the dog family and are not as agile as a cat. They need the 'landing' of the top of a solid fence to land on and push off again. It used to depend on where you lived, but urban foxes are as common as countryside ones and no where is 100% safe. The temporary fencing panels used around building sites make ideal chicken run fencing panels; they are easy to put up and are almost impossible for a fox to scramble over. Remember to get the panels with narrow gaps, there are some with quite wide gaps and the hens walk straight through the fence! See the fox section in Predators and Pests for further fencing advice.

Mud Management

In a restricted area, a grassy surface will soon disintegrate to mud. Straw seems an obvious solution for flooring, but it creates a hard material akin to the wattle and daub used in house building. The hens can build up a mixture on their toes, which forms a hard ball. If this happens it will need to be soaked off and may take more than one go. Under no circumstances try to pull it off, as you will pull her nail off with it. Mud is especially a problem for the fancy varieties of hen with feathered legs. It will need to be brushed off when dry, or washed off if really muddy. It is best not to keep such varieties if mud cannot be avoided.

Wood chippings are a good ground covering, but must be put down on a hard mud base. If there is a wet muddy area the wood chippings will simply disappear into the mud. The chippings will need to be spread quite thickly to have an effect. They can be hosed off if the poo is not power washed off naturally by the rain. I have moved from wood chippings to rubber chippings in my pens and am very pleased with the result. We put a plastic membrane under them and the mud has been banished!

Beg wooden pallets where you see then lying around. The ones with no gaps between the slats are best. These can be used in a patchwork quilt arrangement to make a raised floor to rise above the mud completely. If you can only find ones with gaps between the slats fill the pallets with wood chip to make a solid surface.

Providing a perch in the pen will give the hens the opportunity to perch up out of the mud if they want to. In any event, they will appreciate the perch and will often have an afternoon siesta on it.

Shelter

Chickens do not seem to seek shelter in wet weather. I often look at my bedraggled hens standing in the rain and wonder why they don't hop into the henhouse until the rain has passed. A bushy shrub in the pen, or raising the house high enough of the ground to allow shelter underneath will all help. Wind, though, is a different matter. All poultry seem to hate the wind and need some form of protection. This can be anything from a hedge along one side of the pen to a strategically placed straw bale.

Dust Bath

If the chickens are to be kept in a permanent run you will have to take care to provide the amenities they would have found free ranging in the garden. They will need an area to make a dust bath. If the ground is unsuitable, such as concrete, then provide them with a tray of dry soil. Alternatively, fire cinders are a favourite. Wherever they make their dust bath, sprinkle a good amount of louse powder on it regularly. Thus they will be covering themselves in louse powder each time they use it. After a hen has had a good time flapping about

35

in the dust bath, she will often stand up and shake her feathers back into place, at which point a shower of soil falls to the floor at the same time as a cloud of louse powder rises in to the air. Job done!

Greens

In a permanent run the hens will soon strip the ground bare of grass or foliage, but need to keep up their green intake. Free ranging hens will graze at various heights, depending on the level of the vegetation so try to replicate the variety of height by suspending greens at hen head height, rather than simply throwing them on the floor. Pek-a-Bloks, which are compressed blocks of seed, can be hung up for the same purpose.

Size

The saying goes that size matters. I am often asked about the size of pen required for x number of chickens. My answer is simple: give them the maximum you can. This book assumes that you are keeping a small flock of up to 6 hens to provide enough eggs for your household and maybe a few extra to give away/ sell. I have also assumed that the hens are not in self-contained accommodation which is moved around the garden for the reasons discussed above in the introduction to this chapter.

If you take the example of the Eglu, made by a company called Omlet, it houses up to 4 chickens and has a fixed run attached. The basic run is 5' or 1.5m wide and 10' or 3m long. It can be extended, but that is the basic. Take that as a minimum and anything more you can provide is marvellous.

There is also a warning on making the area too big. One customer was very proud that he had 2 acres of orchard in which the 10 hens he had bought were to free range. A few weeks later he phoned to say he had not had one egg. I told him that they must be laying by now, but just not in the hen house. He assured me that that was not possible as he had watched them and they did not stray far from the house. Another few weeks passed and this time the phone call was a little tetchy as frustration was clearly setting in with the lack of eggs. Again he assured me that there was no possibility of eggs being laid elsewhere. This time I persuaded him to round up family and friends and set off on a 2 acre egg hunt. In a phone call that evening I was advised that the hens were now fenced into a much smaller area!

Wood Chippings

It is important to use the correct form of wood chippings in the run, if that is the form of ground cover you wish to use. One form is a chopped wood and the other is wood chips. Often the two are mixed together. The important word to remember is BARK. The aspergillum fungus loves bark, as it is an ideal medium for it to grow. If the fungus gets into a hen's lungs it will kill her with little or no warning. If she does happen to look off colour, antibiotics will have little effect as the fungus spores can hide in the lung air sacs, which are not helped by the antibiotics. If diagnosed early enough the use of disinfectant F10 under vet's advice can save her, but timing is critical.

Wood chips, with no hint of bark, are fine as they are too hard for the fungus to take a hold.

If you have a memory block in front of the choice of bags in the garden centre, remember that no-one likes a dog BARKing.

The Compost Heap

In the current climate of recycling, local councils are encouraging their residents to cultivate a compost heap. I apologise if I am addressing you as an experienced compost heap owner, but there are two main rules for a successful compost heap or composter. For the usual contents of a heap, such as kitchen waste and used tie bags, the usual compost powder can be added in layers. The powder accelerates the composting and helps keep the odour down. If you are adding the chicken droppings and sawdust from the hen house, then lime should be sprinkled on as well at regular intervals, to neutralise the ammonia in the droppings.

Be vigilant in checking for rat inhabitation as they love compost heaps. The minute you see the telltale round hole take immediate action.

If you are reading this section as a compost heap owner, but not yet a chicken keeper, then your compost heap is fine. However, under the Animal By-Products Regulations 2005 a poultry keeper must only compost in a closed container. There are many types of closed container from the static plastic ones favoured by Councils to the turning drum type in the photo. The point is that there is no access to the compost from wild birds or vermin.

By creating a composter to dispose of the used hen house floor covering you will be creating a first class fertiliser. No more expensive dried chicken dropping pellets from the garden centre, you will have the satisfaction of best quality fertiliser at a fraction of the cost.

A thing of the past

Predators & Pests

There are a number of predators partial to fresh chicken and this chapter gives advice on the best ways of protecting your flock from predator attack.

Birds of Prey

The best known predator is the fox and I will come onto him. Lesser known predators are wild birds of prey, who can pose a real threat to young poultry. They can also scare older ones which can lead to egg laying problems if a laying hen has had a fright. They are a protected species and keeping them out is the only protection. Overhead netting is the best solution, but may not always be practical. The only other solution is some sort of scary device, such as a scarecrow, strips of tinfoil or false bird of prey on a stick, such as a peregrine falcon. Basically, anything which will frighten them off. If the hens are in an open run they need somewhere to be able to run and hide, often under the hen house will be sufficient. They have good all-round vision and will see a bird of prey coming.

Mr and Mrs Fox

The most important criterion in protecting your flock against a fox attack is to ensure that the hen house is impenetrable. Some doors have a wooden block catch which holds the door shut, but security must be bolstered by a brass sliding bolt. A fox pawing at the wooden block closure would be able to swing it around and make the door swing open for him. The same security measures apply to the pop hole or drawbridge in that they can be a weakness in the defense. All this, however, is of no use if they are not closed in time. There is no shortage of foxes in any location and it seems that no mistake will go unpunished. Closing the hens

in at night is essential. It is also a good way of giving responsibility to children, but it should not be completely delegated.

Check the nest box opening and make sure it has a way of being bolted shut. Some have roof which lifts up and this will need a hasp and padlock to ensure security. Basically, make sure that whatever way the nest box opens, the opening can be fastened securely.

Fencing will depend on the set-up you have decided upon, but a security fence needs to be at least 2m high. This will deter most foxes, but a really determined one may scramble over. Foxes are dogs and are not as nimble as a cat, but a foothold will give them a lift. An overhang to the outside at the top of the fence will offer the best defense. Whatever style or height of fence, the bottom of the fence can be dug in, as a fox will think nothing of digging his way in under the fence. Alternatively, fold the fence netting outwards on the floor at right angles to the fence. Pin it down at regular intervals and allow the grass to grow over it. That will also make it difficult for a fox to dig through and is easier to install. There are many types of poultry netting available and if you want to be very thorough, consider electric fencing. When an animal touches the fencing it will get a nasty shock and give the fence a wide berth in future. It is not a fatal shock and the chickens will quickly learn to respect it as well.

Ensure that the fencing around the enclosure has no small holes in it. A fox can squeeze through a remarkably small space. In the photo the fox got in through that small gap at the bottom of the fence, in the middle of the photo.

There are a number of chemical repellents sold to repel foxes, but they are expensive and have to be renewed after rain; this would be an almost permanent pastime in Britain! Foxes don't like dogs, so your family pet will do his bit in fox deterring. Any male members of your family can also contribute to protecting the boundary as foxes are particularly deterred by male urine. This will also need to be repeated after rainfall.

Rats and Mice

Rats and mice pose the next most dangerous threat and are major pests as they are so numerous. As the saying goes, if you see one of them there are sure to be more of them hidden. They are a hazard to the poultry as they carry disease and they pose a threat to human health as well. For man the most serious threat is Weil's disease, a form of jaundice, and if a rat or mice infestation is suspected it is important to wash your hands after touching any surface where they may have been. Any cuts should be washed thoroughly, treated with antiseptic cream and covered with a plaster. There is a statutory duty to keep your garden free of rats and this can be done by calling the Pest Control Officer of the local Council in the event of an infestation, or taking measures yourself by trapping, or poison. The general rule with poison is to double the amount if it has all been taken, until there is some left on the dish. This way you can be sure to have treated all of them. As always, make sure the hens and household pets do not have access to the poison. Prevention is better than cure and simple measures will help in not attracting vermin:

a. Store feed in vermin proof containers. I use black plastic bins because of the clip lids and their resistance to wind. Metal bins with tight fitting lids could be considered better as determined rodents could chew through the plastic if they had a mind to. I have had no damage to mine as yet.

b. Keep the feeding area clean and take up food bowls at night. I just pop them into the relevant black bin for the night.

c. Do not allow areas of standing water and take the water bowls up at night. Bringing them in at night is a good habit to get into, ready to be refilled for the morning.

Rat attack

Predator Identification

Each predator will leave a distinctive trace and can thus be identified. In the unfortunate event of an attack, the predator can be identified and prevention measures taken.

- Head bitten off, bites across the back, lots of deaths, signs of entry, no body, but a mass of feathers: *Fox*

- Flesh eaten off neck, even stripped to the skeleton, eggs broken and licked clean: *Rat*

- Flesh stripped on the neck, holes pecked in eggs or eggs carried away: *Crows, Rooks or Magpies*

- Carcass is nibbled, usually starting at tail end: *Mice*

- Bite marks at the base of the neck and lots of deaths: *Weasel and Stoat*

- Bites around head and neck. Several deaths. No signs of entry: *Mink*

- Total disappearance. No signs of a struggle or entry: *Human*

This last one is a growing threat to poultry keepers and there are thefts of entire poultry flocks being reported as stolen, and in one case I read, complete with housing as well. If you intend to keep rare breeds, poultry security is an issue to be considered alongside your house security provisions.

5

Breeds of Chicken

There are a bewildering number of breeds of chickens. Most of them are listed on the egg colour charts in this book. The breeds typed in bold are the most readily available. This chapter will help you look at the reason for having chickens and the best ones to start with.

Decisions, Decisions

Eggs or eye candy?

When deciding which birds to keep, the starting point is the purpose for keeping them. If you want exotic looking pets and are not too concerned about the egg production, there are some stunning looking 'fancy' chickens. Be aware that the bigger the bird, the more they eat and be prepared for the extra care that a feathered leg bird will need. They do not take so well to muddy conditions and can suffer problems with their legs and feet. The temperament of a breed is also important. A jumpy,

nervous bird will use up more energy and eat more as well as constantly spooking the rest of the flock when she suddenly panics on your approach.

This book is concerned with egg laying chickens and I will concentrate on these. More than that, I believe that the hybrid birds bred specifically for egg production and hardiness, and which have the bonus of being good looking birds, are ideal. See the Preparation for your Hobby section in the Introduction chapter for tips on deciding on the right hen for you.

Finding the chicken of your choice can be difficult. It is no longer possible to buy chickens from breeders at County Shows, and even when it was, they were only annual events. The Poultry Club of Great Britain, *www.poultryclub.org*, has useful advice on breeds and breeders. Magazines such as Country Smallholding and Practical Poultry carry many adverts and putting the required words into

Google can have all sorts of results. Once your desired bird is found, I have discovered that most chicken supplies are invariably miles from you, which involves a long drive to collect them, or a carriage charge.

The Black Rock (sex-link)

The Black Rock is a hybrid and is considered to be the most successful breed bred for free-range conditions. The Black Rock is a true first-cross hybrid from especially selected strains of Rhode Island Red (male line) and a Barred Plymouth Rock (female line). The sex of the chicks can be distinguished at day old, hence the label Sex-Link.

The Black Rock is a particularly hardy bird suitable for the most severe weather conditions. They love being outside whether it is raining, sunny or full snow storm. In the past, I have looked at my chickens in the pouring rain and they look completely bedraggled, but they are happy. It is their thick rich plumage that protects them from the weather. Black Rocks also have a highly developed immune system which not only helps with their hardiness, but also provides a long productive life.

The Black Rock hen produces brown eggs with a good quality of shell, shell colour and size. They should produce 280 plus eggs a year and can easily live for six or more years, continually producing good eggs throughout their life. The quality of eggs from the Black Rock is one of their most notable features. With the right diet you will have eggs with the most fantastic rich yellow yolks.

Black Rocks are often said to be docile birds. They are and they are a pleasure to watch. I also find them fairly intelligent and full of character, but most of all, they are an easy bird to keep. Another important aspect of their character is that they are not easily stressed. Indeed, a few years ago a fox attacked our hens and one was being carried off by the fox, but was saved by our chihuahah. Our poor hen had some feathers and flesh missing, but was soon back happily in the hen house and laying again a few days later. The problem with a nervous bird, apart from being more difficult to keep, is that they will use more energy and therefore food, which means they are more costly to keep.

Black Rocks are bred from a single hatchery in the East of Scotland. Muirfield Hatchery acquired the breeding stock in 1973 and has continued to improve the Black Rock by careful selection without affecting their essential characteristics. With the parent birds being both pure breeds the cross retains superb genetic vigour and excellent health record. There has been no recorded salmonella infection in any U.K. flock and therefore they do not require salmonella vaccines. We buy our hens from an approved agent when they are at point of lay. All chicks are vaccinated at 1 day old for Infectious Bronchitis (I.B.) with H120. A full list of the inoculations administered is at the end of the book.

The Speckledy

The Speckledy is a hybrid bird first bred in 1992 by Stonegate, one of the UK's largest free range egg producers. Back in the early 1990's Stonegate wanted to breed hens that were capable of laying organic eggs that would be accredited by the Soil Association. In order to go organic the company had to rethink completely how it produced eggs and free range hens were a prerequisite. The problem for Stonegate was that they required hens suitable for commercial production and that meant ones that would be prolific layers, producing eggs that were of the highest grade in terms of shell quality, colour and size and all from a free range hen.

Chickens originate from the southern hemisphere where the weather is warm and daylight is a uniform 12 hours throughout the year. Although chickens have been around in the northern hemisphere for thousands of years, most pure breeds still prefer the warmth and daylight. Some of this can be simulated by keeping the birds indoors, but this would negate their free range origin. Stonegate's solution was to use their cross breeding programme to produce a hybrid hen that could thrive in free-range conditions in the less-than-tropical climate of the UK. The birds needed good feather coverage to cope with our weather and they had to be happy foraging for food, and taking full advantage of their free-range conditions. Soil Association rules don't allow beak-tipping (clipping the sharp end off hens' beaks) so the new breed needed to be non-aggressive, too. The initial result was the Speckledy, a chicken which laid dark, shiny-shelled eggs.

A Speckledy Hen is a Rhode Island crossed with a Maran. It resembles a pure Maran in its feathering, but is a more prolific layer, producing dark brown eggs. It is a very docile bird, is easy to manage and is ideal for people looking for something a little special. Due to the nature of its origins it is really only suitable as a free range bird.

Due to its Maran heritage, the Speckledy is a large bird, body weight at 18 weeks is typically 1575g, and will therefore obviously eat more than other breeds. However, the Speckledy is proving ever more popular with small commercial flocks, who like to offer their customers a variety of different coloured eggs. The Speckledy is a dependable layer with a great temperament. A hen will often foster and adopt any orphans and outcasts as her own. They should produce 260+ eggs a year. I get my stock from the same supplier as the Black Rocks and they have the same inoculations.

Columbian Blacktails

These lovely hens have been made famous by Waitrose, who keep flocks of Columbian Blacktails on their farms and are proud to state on their egg boxes that the eggs are from a specific breed of hen. They are a brown chicken with black tips to their tails and black flashes in their wings. Some also have a black necklace and a lace effect to their breast feathers.

Columbian Blacktails are a hybrid between a Rhode Island Red father and a hybrid mother of two strains of Light Sussex. Their black necklace is an obvious trait from the Light Sussex. Their consistent laying of light brown eggs, around 300 a

year, comes from having a Rhode Island Red father. They are easy to manage and adapt well to the circumstances in which they find themselves. They suit a small garden group as well as a larger free ranging flock. They are hardy birds and are able to cope as well with the heat of the summer as they do with the mud and rain of winter. They have a good appetite and certainly cannot be described as picky eaters!

They are a medium sized chicken and lay a good size, strong shelled egg. Columbian Blacktails are an ideal garden chicken.

White Stars

Beware of imitations! The term 'White Star' seems to be attributed to all manner of white chickens. The genuine White Star is a Dutch bred Leghorn hybrid and can lay up to 320 eggs a year. My flock of White Stars has been amazing, even laying consistently throughout the winter months.

They are the smallest of the birds I stock, a slim bird with a distinctive upright tail. As their name implies, they are all white and they lay a beautiful white egg, almost like porcelain in appearance. You will be surprised at the size of egg a White Star can lay, especially when you look at their slim build.

White Stars can be a more nervous bird than the placid Black Rocks or Goldlines and so are not ideal as pets. They do, however, fit happily into any size of flock, from the garden trio to a flock of 50 like mine.

Gold Rangers

This chicken is a Dutch hybrid chicken, a cross between a Rhode Island Red father and a Leghorn mother. These hens can lay up to an amazing 320 light brown coloured eggs a year. They are a brown and white mottled bird.

They are a docile bird, ideal as a pet, as they have a tendency to follow their owner around. They are inquisitive and will happily visit you in the kitchen if they are lucky enough to find the door open. They are an economical bird to keep and fit well into any size flock. Gold Rangers are hardy and adaptable, making them an ideal starter bird.

Amber Stars and Silver Stars

These are Rhode Island White based hybrid with extremely soft feathering. They lay brown eggs and maintain an excellent shell quality. They are docile birds and suitable as pets.

Cream Legbars

Cream Legbars have been described as 'a blue egg laying autosexing pure breed of chicken.' Let's look at that in more detail.

The start of the breed can be attributed to Clarence Elliott. His passion was rare plants and he travelled widely in search of new and rare species of plant. He returned from such a trip to Patagonia with the extra bonus of three hens and a cockerel. The cockerel did not survive, but the three hens made their way to Professor R C Punnett at Cambridge University. He was studying poultry genetics and experimented with the cross breeding of these Patagonian hens. The breed was further developed in the 1930's using Brown Leghorns, Barred Rocks and Araucanas. It is a breed, rather than a hybrid, because the chicks are the same as the adults, as their chicks will be, and so on. A hybrid is the first breeding each time between the two breeds chosen to create the hybrid and the chicks cannot, by definition, be the same as the parents.

The heritage of the Araucana gives the Cream Legbar the ability to lay blue, sometimes olive, eggs. It also accounts for the 'hat' or 'pompom' the hens have on their heads. The Leghorn heritage is clear from the large, floppy comb on the Cream Legbars. The Legbar half of their name derives from their heritage: 'Leg' from the Brown Leghorns and 'bar from the Barred Rocks. The Barred Rock was used because of its egg laying qualities and hardy nature.

The autosexing, nothing to do with breeding techniques, relates to the instantly recognisable distinction between the sexes as soon as they hatch. The surprising bit for the bird world is that the girls are by far the most striking with dark stripes on a yellow background and a wonderful sweep of dark eye liner, whereas the cockerels are almost plain yellow.

The chicks grow into very pretty hens and quite striking cockerels. They are a slender bird and smaller than most traditional breeds. They have a fairly long, upright tail and carry their wing tucked close to their body. They have red skin on their faces and yellow beak, legs and feet.

Cream Legbars are an alert breed and quick on their feet. They are small enough to be kept in an enclosed run, such as the ones attached to commercially built hen houses or arks. They can be kept in a larger pen if there is no need to catch them as they are so nimble they are virtually impossible to catch! Imprinting them to the henhouse is therefore vital at the outset!

Cuckoo Marans

The Marans is believed to originate from the French town of Marans, near La Rochelle, on the Atlantic coast. Its origins can be traced back to the 12th century when Henry II married Aleanour of Aquitaine, who brought with her a good section of the South West of France. English domination of this area lasted 2 centuries and during that time English ships would dock in La Rochelle. Surviving fighting cocks, taken on board for 'in voyage entertainment', were off loaded and hens were taken on board to provide eggs and meat. This interchange of chickens, and the introduction of the fighting cockerels to the wild hen population, led to the Maran breed and accounts for the sometimes aggressive nature displayed by the cockerels. Our cockerel, Rambo, is as sweet as can be, but does possess an impressive set of spurs, another legacy from his fighting cock heritage.

The breed was largely untouched until the second half of the 19th century when a French breeder, Louis Rouille, brought Langshan chickens from Asia, famed for dark brown eggs, and farmed them in Fouras, very near La Rochelle. The colour of the egg is passed from the cockerel to his daughters. Escapee cockerels from the farm found their way to the wild Marans of La Rochelle and the result was the now trademark dark brown egg.

Marans were first shown at the National Exhibition in La Rochelle in 1914. They created great interest because of the dark egg, but there was a large variety in the colour of the hens. In 1929 an Englishman, Lord Greenway, attended the Paris Exhibition and was so taken by the Marans that he brought some back to England and set about selectively breeding them to standardise the colour. He reduced the colour range to dark cuckoo, silver cuckoo and golden cuckoo. A colour standard was defined and published by the French Authorities in 1931.

The popularity of the Marans continued until after the 1939/1945 war, but then suffered a decline as other breeds were introduced. It didn't disappear because of the very dark brown egg and its dual capacity as a meat bird. It had one big disadvantage as the poultry world became more commercial in that the chicks were impossible to sex until they were much older. Whilst the cockerels can be kept for meat, this is a specialised area and they are far more costly to rear than the commercial meat hybrids. In order to develop chicks which could be sexed on hatching, Light Sussex hens were introduced and the resultant offspring were mated back to the Marans. Thus the colour of the bird did not change, but the chicks are now distinguishable as the hens are darker than the cockerels. The

disadvantage of this is that the birds with the Light Sussex strain lay a lighter colour egg and generations with this strain will continue to do so. As they look exactly the same, there is a current danger of the dark brown egg feature being lost. However, our cockerel, Rambo, is proven to pass the dark egg shell power on to his daughters.

Light Sussex

It is believed that the origins of the Light Sussex go back to the time of the Roman invasion of England, when chickens were brought here through the

Roman Empire from Indo-China. It is also thought that the Romans brought them in from the Ardennes region of Belgium. Either way it is agreed that the Romans imported them.

It is a heavy breed bird and was primarily kept for its meat. It has a large frame and has the capacity to put on a large amount of meat. A cockerel will reach 9/10lb in weight and a hen 7lb. It is a slow growing bird, which is reputed to give a better flavour than the fast growing hybrids used today. The Light Sussex is classified as 'heavy – soft feather'.

As an egg layer it lays a light brown egg and can lay up to 220 eggs a year.

The Light Sussex is a popular chicken because of its calm and friendly temperament. It is an ideal garden chicken and very hardy despite the softness of its feathers.

How to Tell the Difference Between Girl and Boy Chicks

Sex link hybrids have been specifically bred to distinguish the boys from the girls on day one. Traditional breeds are more difficult to differentiate until the different feather coats are through. Some traits can give an indication.

Colour of legs: If a dark leg male is mated with light leg hens they tend to produce boy chicks with light legs and girl chicks with dark legs. It sounds easy, but it can be difficult to tell the leg colour early on.

Size of legs: Boys generally have thicker, stockier legs then the girls. This difference becomes evident as they grow, and spotting the difference becomes easier with experience.

Length of primary feathers: The wing primary feathers grow quicker on a girl than a boy. This requires comparison between siblings and obviously can't be done until the feathers have started to grow.

Colour of eyes: Dark eyed males crossed with light eyed females tend to produce dark eyed girls and light eyes boys.

Yellow Spot on Head: Boys have a large yellow spot and girls have a small yellow spot on their head.

6

Getting Home

Transporting your newly acquired chickens and introducing them to their new home and routine is the most exciting part. This chapter shows you the correct way to do it and following the guidelines will ensure safe and happy Chicken Keeping for you and your family.

Travel Container

Chickens are best transported in a dark environment, such as a closed cardboard box or an animal carrier with a blanket over it. They must not be able to get out, but be able to breathe! When you get home take the container straight to the hen house, don't open it on the way as they can jump out in a flash. For the same reason, open the box in the hen house itself. The chickens should be left in the open box to come out on their own, young ones especially may take a while to feel confident.

Imprinting

The chickens need to be 'imprinted' with the identity of their new home. The length of time to leave them in the house depends on what time of the day you get them home, but anytime after mid-day I would leave them there until the morning after next. That is assuming they have not had a long journey or been away from food and water for any length of time before you get them. If that is the case, they should be given access to food and water before being

shut in. If you have them in the morning, then shut them in for most of the day and let them out for food and water a few hours before dusk. If they do not go to bed on their own at dusk, they will need to be shooed in, or caught and put in. If that is the case, then leave them until lunchtime the next day. Expect this for the next few days if they don't automatically put themselves to bed. Even if they don't immediately get the hang of putting themselves to bed at dusk, they will do so within a few days. Imprinting is vital; otherwise they will happily perch in the trees and be easy prey for a fox. The chickens in the picture on the left got the hang of putting themselves to bed in the hen house eventually!

Shutting the henhouse at night is vital. Although they put themselves to bed, they must be shut in, for fear of a fox attack. Foxes can attack during the day, but the greatest risk is during the hours of darkness.

Catching A Chicken

The easiest way to catch a chicken is to grab a leg. They can be carried upside down by holding both feet, but I prefer to carry them the right way up on my arm if they are calm. If you do carry them by the feet, put one finger between their legs so that their legs are not squeezed together as that hurts the hen. Under no circumstances carry a hen by just one leg. Their hips can dislocate very easily.

Hens have long sharp nails which can rip your clothing if the hen struggles whilst held under your arm. If you have a struggling chicken it is best to keep hold of her feet and hold her upside down, as she will stop struggling immediately. If holding a chicken in your hands, rather than under your arm, it is important to hold her tight enough to pin her wings down, but not too tight. When they become tame, they will often squat down in front of you and then it is easy to pick them up.

The best way to carry a chicken is on your arm with her head pointing to your elbows. Hold her feet with your hand and she will sit there comfortably. Her feet and rear end are both facing away from you, the best way to face! The chap in this picture has mastered it perfectly.

Talk To Them

Once they are imprinted they will soon settle into the daily routine. They will also soon associate you with food and come running towards you. Mine even flap their wings to help them run faster when they see me coming. Talk to them and you will find that they respond. At night I call 'Good night Girls' as I shut the henhouse door and they 'bauk, bauk' back. Give them a collective name to call them, I call mine, 'chouk chouks', and you will be surprised at how obedient they can become.

As you observe them you will notice that they talk to each other as well. They have a number of call signals from the contented cluck, cluck to themselves as they go through their day to specific calls with a message. They will emit a shrill shriek on the sight of a predator and signal to each other if they have found a tasty morsel. I often notice in the morning, if I have been late filling an empty water drinker the first one to find it filled will make a sort of cluck and the others will immediately come running over to her. Young ones will shout "ow, ow" as they are caught and sound as if someone is killing a cat, which can cause a little concern to the first time buyer.

Wing Clipping

If your chickens are in anything other than an enclosed pen, they will need their wings clipping. Their natural instinct is to roost as high up as possible, which will be up a tree if one is handy. If you are going to clip their wings do it as soon as you get them home and before you let them out of the henhouse. The phrase "a bird in the hand is worth two in a bush" is a good saying here, as if you don't do it immediately you will have to catch a fully flighted bird later, maybe even from a neighbour's garden or the tallest tree. Generally it is only necessary to do one wing, as it puts them off balance for flying. For my young point of lays I clip both wings, as they are so light they can jump/fly up to quite a height. Clipping a wing is easy and does not hurt the chicken at all; it is just like clipping fingernails. Holding the chicken sideways on a surface spread out the wing on the side way from you. Starting from the tip of her wing, separate the first ten feathers and cut straight across them with a pair of scissors, about halfway down the feathers. Use the tips of the smaller feathers, which overlap at the top of the large feathers, as a cutting guide. The wings may need to be clipped again when new feathers have grown after a moult, but usually the hens are well established in their routine by then and have no desire to escape.

Louse Powder

Whilst you have a grip of the chicken it is a good idea to dust her with louse powder as a precaution. The only accessible patch of skin is her 'armpit', so lift up a wing and give a liberal shake of louse powder under her wing. Massage the powder along her side, back and bottom. Do the same the other side. By then the chicken, your hands and the surface you are using will all be covered in powder, but the job is done.

I use louse powder as a preventative measure. I put it on the chickens when they first arrive and would advise you to do the same when they arrive with you. Use the powder in the nest boxes when you clean them out and in the dirt bath area they use. Each time they use the dirt bath, they are flicking more louse powder over themselves. Every little helps.

Pecking Order

Hens naturally have a pecking order. 'Pecking order' is a firmly established phrase in the English language, as is 'hen pecked' and both are a reality in keeping hens. In a small flock of 2 or 3 it may not be noticeable, but in a larger

64

number of hens a 'head hen' will emerge. The others will defer to her, especially over food and will eat when she moves on.

Head hen is A and the pecking order works its way down. In a flock of 5, for example, A will peck at all 4. Hen B will peck at C, D and E. Hen C will peck at D an E, and so on. So long as E accepts that she is at the end of the pecking order all will be fine. It is when she doesn't that the squabbling starts and goes on until the pecking order is re-established.

Hens will soon pick on a weaker member of the flock and the head hen will think nothing of taking a good peck at a weaker bird, or a newcomer, often getting a beakful of feathers. The attacked hen will let out a squawk, but will come to no other harm. She will have had her card marked and will know where she is in the pecking order. If, however, there is a continued series of squawks then serious bullying is going on. There are two options in this case; one is to remove the bullied hen to a place of safety and the other is to deal with the bully. The easiest way to deal with a bully in my experience is to remove her for a few days. This allows the pecking order to readjust and she will find it hard to re-establish herself on the new order. Making her squat, by pushing her down gently, will also take a bully down a peg or two.

In either situation, if a hen is removed from the flock, she should be held where she and they can still see each other. That way, she is not a complete stranger when she is reintroduced.

The same applies when introducing new chickens. A minimum of two should be introduced as they can stick together in the face of adversity. A new chicken on her own can be unmercifully picked on. Introductions will be easier if other newcomers can be held in a pen within sight of the main flock. Integrating, say a week later, will be much easier. This is because hens recognise each other by their combs and the flock will half recognise the newcomers as they have already seen them for a distance.

Hook Farm

7

Feeding

Fat hens don't lay! This chapter will tell you how to keep your hens fit and healthy and may contain a few surprises. You don't have to get up at 6am every morning to feed them, really you don't!

It is important that your chickens have a balanced diet. They will fill up on tasty scraps and corn first, if given the opportunity, so the trick is to make the nutritious food freely available and to restrict or eliminate the bulky food. A balanced diet, as for humans, consists of proteins, carbohydrate, fats, minerals, vitamins and water.

Digestive System

A hen will hold an amount of grit and crushed oyster shell in her crop. There is also a small quantity of grit in her stomach. The hen will fill up with food in the morning, graze throughout the day and fill up again with corn or wheat in the evening. The food first goes into the crop, where it is ground by the crop's muscles contracting and relaxing, using the grinding action of the grit to break down the food. A food syrup is made, which is slowly released from the crop unto the stomach. Once the crop is full from her first fill of the day, the hen will need to stop eating for a while until there is space in the crop to allow her to eat again. It is a continuous process, so more often than not the crop will be full. By the same token, it will be rare for the crop to be empty. It is therefore important that there is enough food in the feeder to last the whole day as the hen will fill her crop up as soon as possible and then top up with food every so often as the crop empties a little.

A typical pellet feeder. This one holds 1.5 kg of pellets and is suitable for feeding 2 to 3 chickens.

A typical plastic drinker. This one holds 1.3 litres of water and is suitable for 2 to 3 chickens.

Layers Pellets

The main food to give your chickens is layers pellets and or layers mash. They are compound feeds providing all the goodness the chicken needs. They contain 16% protein as well as fibre, Vitamins A, D3 and E and minerals. They are both about the same price by weight, so the choice whether to feed either or both is yours. The pellets can be given in a bowl or in a pellet feeder. The bowl needs to be non-tip, so should have a wide base and be heavy, such as ceramic, as the chickens will push it around as they eat. The bowl shouldn't have a rim,

otherwise the hens will step on it and tip the bowl up. The important thing with both the pellets and the mash is to make sure they are under cover from the rain. I use a child's plastic play table over my food station.

Layers Pellets

Layers Mash

This has the same nutritional content as the pellets, but is in powder form. The mash can be given dry, or mixed with water to make a sort of porridge. A traditional alternative to this is to mix the mash with mashed potato. However, the mashed potato mix should not be given too often, as the potato will bulk the chicken up without giving much nutrition. Dry layers mash can be wasteful, as they don't tend to pick up any that falls out of the bowl, but I prefer it as any uneaten dry mash can be used the next day. Mash mixed with something else has to be prepared freshly daily and any left over at the end of the day, assuming the chickens have not been as greedy as they can be, should be thrown away.

The dry mash should be given in a heavy, flat based, non-rimmed bowl as described above.

Layers Mash

Mash and pellets, basically, do the same job and therefore you can use one or the other, but I find that my chickens like both; they enjoy their food and seem to like variety in the same way that we do. Both should be offered in containers big enough to ensure there is food available throughout the day. The containers should be collected at night so as not to attract any vermin.

Wheat And Mixed Corn

Grain, such as wheat or mixed corn, should be given in the afternoon / evening to give the bird a full crop for the night. It shouldn't be given in the morning as they will fill up on it and don't want the nutritious pellets and mash. Wheat is better than mixed corn for most of the year, as it is not so fattening. If a chicken puts on too much internal weight, it could affect egg production. The average Black Rock will eat around 15 grams of grain a day. I suggest you weigh some out so that you know what the total daily ration is for your flock in handfuls or scoopfuls. Keeping to the correct ration will help keep your chickens at full laying potential. The wheat can simply be thrown on the ground as the chickens like foraging for it. In the winter, laying hens will need to increase their food in order to keep warm. At this time they appreciate mixed corn as they like the soya and maize which makes up the mixed corn. These two last ingredients are more fattening than the wheat, which is why it is not advisable to use mixed corn routinely, but they give

Elements of a Good Diet

Clean, fresh water during the day.

Layers Pellets and/or Mash fed in the mornings to provide the full balance of nutrients.

Wheat or Mixed Corn in the afternoon or evening to provide a full crop for the night.

Crushed Oyster Shell providing calcium for good eggs.

Poultry Spice for improving all round condition.

Poultry Drink feed supplement f or providing good condition and appetite.

Grit available to help with digestion.

Mixed Corn

the chickens the extra fat they need to keep them warm and egg producing in the cold months. With either wheat or corn, make sure you feed a restricted amount; treat them like cream cakes and chocolate and give the chickens as much chocolate as you would allow children to have. Do not allow ad lib feeding as with the mash and pellets.

Wheat

Crushed Oyster Shell And Grit

The chickens need to pick up grit to enable their crop and stomachs to grind the grain and oyster shell. They will find some in the soil they are on and if they are not on soil there is some grit in the pellets and mash, but wherever they are, it is best to give them some grit in a bowl to be certain they have some available. The chickens also need crushed oyster shell and the commercially available oyster shell is mixed with grit, thereby providing both at the same time. The oyster shell is ground down in the crop at the same time as the food and provides calcium for their own bone structure and for egg shell formation. A lack of calcium can lead to egg shell problems, such as eggs with a deformed shell or even no shell at all. It can also lead to egg eating as the chickens eat the shells to try to make up for the calcium deficiency they are suffering. Traditionally, shells were fed back to the chickens

Crushed Oyster Shell with Grit

before crushed oyster shell became commercially available. You can still feed your chickens egg shells, but they must be baked at 170 degrees centigrade for 10 minutes to remove the mineral oil coat and make them brittle enough crush. They must be crushed so that the chickens don't recognise them and associate them with their own eggs. This in turn could encourage them to eat their own eggs, which is the last thing you want!

The crushed oyster shell and grit can be thrown on the ground in the same way as the wheat, to encourage the hens to forage, but this can be wasteful. Unlike wheat, where the chickens will not leave an uneaten grain if you give them the right amount, they only pick up the crushed oyster shell and grit when they need it. Any unused surplus will get lost in the ground and therefore wasted. You can put a sprinkling on the dry mash in the morning and if they don't want it, it is left in the bowl. Alternatively, leave the grit and oyster shell in a separate heavy, non-rimmed bowl. It will stay there for what seems like a long time until suddenly you notice that the bowl is empty.

> ## Feeding Programme
>
> **Morning** – Fill feeder with layers pellets and or bowl with layers mash. Clean and fill drinker. Give crushed oyster shell if needed. I mix a little with the mash. Suspend fresh greens for them to peck at.
>
> Provide poultry drink and poultry spice as required.
>
> **Afternoon** – Feed wheat or mixed corn on the ground.
>
> **Evening** – Remove feeder and drinker for the night, to be replaced in the morning. This will stop free meals for other birds and rodents.

Poultry Spice

Poultry spice, a mineral based supplement, is recommended for improving all round condition. It helps feather formulation and growth and in particular it is very good at

Poultry Spice

helping chickens to get quickly over a moult. It is invaluable if you are rearing chickens. It is a powder, which can be sprinkled over the pellets, but is best mixed in with the mash.

Kelp Seaweed Powder

Kelp Seaweed powder is actually used as an agricultural fertilizer, but it contains many trace elements and a high proportion of iodine. The iodine enhances the keratin (protein) in a hen's feather. It is particularly useful during a hen's moult and can be given at any time feather condition does not look its best. It can be put in a separate dish so that the hens can help themselves whenever they feel they need the feather boost. It can be obtained from agricultural suppliers.

Olive Oil

Hens, like us, make Vitamin D from sunlight. During the dark winter months it is a good idea to add a spoonful of cod liver oil to their food every so often, just to supplement the Vitamin D in the absence of sunlight.

Fresh Water

Fresh water, changed daily, must be available at all times throughout the day. During winter, you may need to check the water a couple of times a day to ensure that it has not frozen. A Black Rock will drink 200ml of water a day. In hot weather, this can double. In summer some people add cider vinegar to the water at a rate of 10ml per gallon to reduce bacterial growth in the water. Poultry drink can be added to the water every so often. It contains

iron as a ready absorbent phosphate in a syrup base and helps maintain good condition and appetite.

Water Source

If the food station is near the house it is easy to carry a full drinker out to the food station. If, however, it is a distance from the house, then it may be more convenient to run a hosepipe up there. If you attach a hosepipe to an outside tap it has to have a non return valve fitted between the tap and the hosepipe. From the 1st January 1989, Water Bye-Law 18 came into effect. This requires any outside with a hosepipe fitted to it to be protected from the dangers of contaminated water being siphoned back into the mains. Non compliance can result in heavy fines.

A watering can kept specifically for the hens can be a very good way of getting water to the food station. I have a hosepipe up to the hen pens and turn it on every other day. On a water day I use the watering can to fill the drinkers and the fill it a second time for use the next day, when the hose pipe won't be on.

Scraps

Scraps can no longer be fed to the chickens. Some go so far as to say that scraps are only good for the compost heap. The rule is that if it has been in the kitchen it cannot be fed to the chickens. Fresh fruit and veg, however, whether from the garden or shop are of great benefit. Greens help the yolk colour and add to a balanced diet with their mineral content. The chickens love lettuce and tomato as well as apples and broccoli. They like most fruit and vegetables,

except citrus fruits. Be careful of stringy vegetables such as celery and cabbage, as the strings can get caught up in the crop and stop the food passing into the stomach. Celery should have the strings removed in the same way as we prepare it for ourselves and stringy cabbage should be tied together and suspended in the pen so that the hens can just peck at it. This also adds interest at head height, rather than on the floor.

Siting The Food Station

Their food and water should be raised off the ground to prevent pollution from mud, wood shavings, etc. Hens also appreciate feeding and drinking at a comfortable height. I put mine on a pallet under the plastic table, but a breeze block or a couple of bricks will do. It is best to bring the water and feeders in at night. It is essential to bring the water drinker in during winter as it is guaranteed to be frozen in the morning. Freezing the plastic drinker makes the plastic brittle and easily broken. It will need to be defrosted before taking the bottom off

My Feed Station. The table keeps the feed dry and the pallet keeps the food off the ground so saving it from being spoilt by the mud

to refill it. This is bound to happen on a morning when you are running late. Another alternative for the water is to have two drinkers, thus you can take one out fresh each morning and bring the other one in ready for the next day. Emptying the food feeder at night will prevent the wild birds having a free meal and not encourage any passing rodents. I just pop the food bowls into the food plastic clip bin at night. Make it part of your 'bedtime'routine.

If you have a number of chickens two food stations will be a good idea. Bullying is more prevalent in a bigger group and a bully will find it more difficult to defend two food stations than just one. Also, each size feeder will only comfortably fit a certain number around them at one time, usually in the first morning rush. If there is pushing and shoving at one, then it is best to have two.

Food Storage

On the subject of rodents, food storage has to be carefully considered. Convenience means that it is kept outside, near the chickens, in which case it needs to be predator (rodent) and weather proof. I use clip lid, black plastic bins, kept in the shade. I know a determined rodent could gnaw its way into a plastic bin, but I have had no problems. Metal dustbins are available, but they are too cold to the touch in winter and too hot to the touch in summer. The alternative is to keep the food store in the house. The predator proof criterion still exists in a shed, out house or garage. Wherever it is kept, it has to be out of direct sun light as heating the food will break down the nutritional content.

Poisonous Plants

Shrubs and plants that are known to be poisonous to poultry are detailed below. The pictures are a general guide as there can be many varieties of the same plant.

Bryony, Bryonia cretica

Perennial climbing herb of the Gourd Family - up to 4 m. Slim, bristly, weak stems. Leaves with five lobes, opposite to non - ligneous tendrils. Pale green flowers. The fruit is a red berry about 1 cm in diameter.

Deadly Nightshade, Atropa belladonna

Coarse, branched, perennial herb with red sap; leaves alternate, simple; flowers axillary, drooping, tubular, 5-lobed, dull red-purple or greenish purple; fruit a glossy, purple-black berry.

Hemlock, Conium maculatum

The name "poison hemlock" refers to two entirely different poisonous herbs (Conium, pictured here, and Cicuta) that, if eaten, can cause convulsions, respiratory arrest, damage to the central nervous system, and death. Native to Europe and the United States, these plants range in size from 5 cm to 3 m (2 in to 10 ft).

Horseradish, Armoracia rusticana

Horseradish is a perennial plant of the Brassicacaea family, which includes mustard and cabbages. The plant is probably native to southeastern Europe and western Asia, but is popular around the world today. It grows up to 1.5 metres (five feet) tall and is mainly cultivated for its large white, tapering root, although the leaves are also edible.

Laburnum, Laburnum anagyroides

They have yellow pea-flowers in pendulous racemes 10–30 cm long in spring, which makes them very popular garden trees. In L. anagyroides the racemes are 10–20 cm long, with densely packed flowers; in L. alpinum the racemes are 20–30 cm long, but with the flowers sparsely along the raceme. The leaves are trifoliate, somewhat like a clover, the leaflets typically 2–3 cm long in L. anagyroides and 4–5 cm long in L. alpinum.

Monkshood, Aconitum napellus

They are distinguished by having one of the five petaloid sepals called the galea, in the form of a cylindrical helmet; hence the English name monkshood. There are 2–10 petals, in the form of nectaries. The two upper petals are large. They are placed under the hood of the calyx and are supported on long stalks.

Privet, Lingustrum vulgare

Privet was originally the name for the European semi-evergreen shrub Ligustrum vulgare. Used extensively for privacy hedging (hence "privet", private). The term is now used for all members of the genus Ligustrum, which includes about 40–50 species of evergreen, semi-evergreen or deciduous shrubs and small trees.

Rhubarb, Rheum

Rhubarb is a perennial plant that grows from thick short rhizomes, comprising the genus Rheum. The large, somewhat triangular leaf blades are elevated on long, fleshy petioles. The flowers are small, greenish-white, and borne in large compound leafy inflorescences. Rhubarb leaves contain poisonous substances. Rhubarb leaf poisoning is most often caused by oxalic acid, a corrosive and nephrotoxic that is abundantly present in a lot of plants.

Yew, Taxus baccata

It is a small to medium-sized evergreen tree, growing 10–20 m tall, exceptionally up to 28 m. It is relatively slow growing, but can be very long-lived, with the maximum recorded trunk diameter of 4 m probably only being reached in around 4,000 years. It has thin scaly brown bark. The leaves are lanceolate, flat, dark green, 1–4 cm long and 2–3 mm broad, arranged spirally on the stem, but with the leaf bases twisted to align the leaves in two flat rows either side of the stem except on erect leading shoots where the spiral arrangement is more obvious.

Photo by Stéphane Rocher

8

Hen Health

This chapter will help you keep your hens in tip top condition with tips on what to look out for as well as a number of preventative measures to take as the seasons change.

Health Check

In the hen world it is essential to keep your position in the pecking order. Any sign of weakness or illness will result quickly in loss of position and even bullying from the others, who don't want a sick member in their flock. For this reason, a hen can keep up appearance until she really is at death's door. It is important to get to know your hens and visually check them daily. Every so often handle them for a moment just to check that they aren't wasting away under all those feathers. When a tame hen squats in front of you, instead of stepping over her, just pick her up for a moment. A sick chicken that has missed detection will eventually stand in a hunched position away from the main flock, often listless and showing no interest in life. Consult the Troubleshooting section for more detail and action required.

The normal temperature of a hen is 103 degrees. To take her temperature, simply insert a thermometer in her vent for a minute or two. Any deviation from her normal temperature will indicate a problem.

Hybrids are usually vaccinated against the main diseases. The appendix gives the vaccination programme they will probably have been through. When buying chickens it is important to establish their health history and their immune protection, so ask questions. It is also important to establish their age as chickens have all the eggs they are going to lay in their left ovary when they hatch. (Their right ovary is not used.) At any time after point of lay they will have one egg less a day to provide for you. A young bird is easy to tell as she is light, her wattle and comb are not fully grown and her leg scales will be small and perfectly smooth. Once a hen is past that point of lay stage though, and she is at laying weight I find it very difficult to tell the age of a hen. The stage of feather growth (see the feather section in the Introduction) will date a young bird, but, as with her wattle and comb, once her adult feathers are through it is difficult to tell her adult age. Having said that, if a hen is in moult she is at least a year old. I use coloured leg rings, a different colour for each batch to tell mine apart.

The Moult

The annual moult takes place as the days become shorter, August to December, and can last up to 3 months. Some lose feathers over time and others seem to lose them overnight. Egg laying will stop at this time and will not resume until the hen is in full feather again. A hen has between 8,500 and 9,000 feathers! The birds which lose the most feathers are said to be the best layers. As the hen gets older she will lose fewer feathers each time. In full moult the hen will

look very tatty and will benefit from extra supplements, such as Poultry Spice, to help grow healthy feathers back. Alternatively, give them a Kelp Seaweed Powder as the iodine it contains reacts with the protein in the feather and thus improves the structure and strength of the feathers. If a hen has an extra long moult or moults out of season, this can indicate an excess of amino acids in the feed. It would be worth checking the food content if it is your usual food and going back to your usual food if you have changed. Hens kept inside will have a tendency for a longer moult. Free ranging access to fresh air and fun outside is a much better environment for them.

How To Tell If A Hen Is In Lay

How yellow is her face?

In yellow skinned breeds of hen, such as Rhode Island Reds, the yellow pigment can be seen in the legs and feet, ear lobe, eyelids, beak and vent. When the pullet comes into lay the yellow colour will be deposited in these areas. As she lays her eggs the pigment gradually diminishes, but in a definite order. After the first few eggs, the edges of the vent will be paler, then the eyelids and ear lobes. The beak is next, starting at the base and working out towards the tip. Finally her feet and legs lose the yellow and become whiter, starting at her toenails and ending at the top of her legs. The whole process takes 4 to 6 months, the longer it takes, the better layer the hen. The hen ceases to lay for a while and the yellow pigment is replenished in the same order as it was lost. The refilling is a quicker process than the loss, and, once replenished, the cycle starts again.

How red is her comb?

As a hen comes into lay her comb will become bright red and stay that way when she is in good health and laying. The colour and state of her comb can tell you a lot about the state and health of a hen. See the introduction section for more on combs.

Is her pelvis wide enough?

If you first locate the hen's vent, you will find two bones which stick out either side of the vent and just below it. If they are tight together the hen is a young bird. The pins will gradually grow apart and once you can get 2 fingers between them, then she is laying. This is the ultimate test and if she is laying and there are still no eggs in the house: go hunting!

Seasonal Precautions

Summer

In summer the hens will need shade from the fierce overhead sun. Having said that, they will enjoy sun bathing, lying on one side with a wing outstretched, catching the rays, so the pen mustn't be in permanent shade. When they get too hot, the only patch of bare skin is under their wings, so the only opportunity to cool down by sweating it to stand with their wings held out to allow air to their skin. They will also stand with their beaks open, almost as if panting.

Their water supply will also need to be kept as cool as possible, as a lack of cool water can lead to egg eating. Place the water container in as shady place as possible and try to change the water more frequently on particularly hot days. At least once a day the water should be completely changed, even if the container is not empty.

In summer, check that the food store is not in full sunlight, as the heat can break down the nutritional content of the food.

Also, try to collect the eggs two, or even three times during the height of summer. Eggs need to be stored in cool conditions as soon as possible.

The summer months will see the height of the red mite infestations. Be sure to check the house regularly and take immediate action as soon as there is any sign of them.

Winter

As autumn arrives take the time to check the hen house for leaks and draughts. Your hens will appreciate dry and draught-free accommodation even more during the winter months. Also check that the house has been sited with its back to the prevailing wind.

In winter, the main enemy is the frost. Birds with large combs can be susceptible to frostbite. A precautionary film of Vaseline will help prevent a frostbite attack.

Frost is also a problem with the water supply and the drinkers. Get into the habit of bringing the drinker in at night ready to be refilled and taken out in the morning. This will prevent the plastic from becoming brittle and cracking in the frost. Even with precautions, it is always best to have a spare drinker on hand for that morning when it does crack. There are metal drinkers available which are obviously not susceptible to cracking in frost. The disadvantage with metal drinkers, I feel, is that they are so cold to the touch in winter. It is not pleasant for us to touch ice cold metal and I do not think it is pleasant for the hens either.

The hens will need extra food to help them cope with the cold. Keep an eye on the feeding bowls and if they are empty each evening, give them a little extra in the mornings. An extra handful of corn on the very cold days will be well received.

Remember that food will be getting scarcer for the fox as winter sets in. Shutting the hens in as soon as they go to bed will be a priority now. By the same token, don't let them out too early in the morning as foxes can still be out at first light. In mid-winter it can be dark by 3pm, so try to make arrangements to shut them in early. Consider an automatic pop-hole opener and closer, if you are not able to shut them in until later. Rats and mice will be looking for warm winter quarters and are not to be encouraged. Keep up the practice of taking the feeding bowls away at night and be prepared to trap or poison any rodents who take up residence.

Rats and mice will be looking for warm winter quarters and are not to be encouraged. Keep up the practice of taking the feeding bowls away at night and be prepared to trap or poison any rodents who do take up residence.

Chickens are horrified at the sight of snow! Instead of the usual scramble out of the hen house in the morning when the door is flung open they all just stand in the doorway, unsure of the sight in front of them. When they do eventually venture out it is almost on tiptoe. Egg production seems to drop dramatically on snow bound days.

Troubleshooting

9

This chapter covers the common problems and ailments encountered by the small chicken keeper. It is not intended to put you off having a few chickens, quite the opposite, it is intended to enable to keep chickens with confidence, knowing that you will know what to do in the unlikely event that one of your hens has a problem.

Initial Diagnosis

There are a few basic questions with which to start your diagnosis and decide on what action to take. Is a single bird affected or are a number of hens looking unwell? If it is one bird then it is likely to be something to have affected her, such as a fright leading to being egg bound, an impacted crop or infections such as peritonitis. If a number are affected it could be some kind of infectious disease.

Has the decline been progressive, or overnight? Sudden illness will indicate a severe infection. Longer declines can be longer developing diseases, such as Mareks or Coccidiosis. A group decline may also be due to the quality of feed they are getting, or not, as the case may be, and to the standard of hygiene in their environment.

Is the problem respiratory? There are a number of symptoms, such as caked nostrils, blood-shot or watery eyes, swelling of the cheeks, head shaking, gasping breathing, sneezing or bubbles forming on the nostrils as they breathe. Is their breathing noisy? Respiratory diseases, such as Mycoplasma, infectious bronchitis and fungal infections will need correct diagnosis by a vet in order to protect the rest of the flock and decide the fate of an infected hen.

What colour and consistency are the droppings? Are there worms evident in the droppings? Is there diarrhoea and if so, what colour is it? Is the crop distended? These symptoms indicate a digestive upset which could be caused by parasitic infections such as Coccidiosis, Salmonella or a viral infection. Nutrition may also play a part, such as a sudden change in diet, or something that has disagreed with them in the kitchen scraps you have given them. See the Feeding chapter for do's and don'ts on scraps.

Is there a change in behaviour? Have they suddenly become aggressive with each other or uneasy together? Has feather pecking started? Is there paralysis or unusual movements? Behavioural changes can be caused by various parasites and diseases such as Fowl Pest, Infectious Bronchitis or Mareks disease. It could simply be a nutritional issue where there is not enough to go around.

Insufficient protein in the diet can lead to feather pecking as feathers contain protein and the hen tries to supplement her intake this way.

Finally, has egg production changed? Have the colour or shape of eggs changed? Is the shell of normal quality? Is the white of an egg you have broken too runny? These are all symptoms of a change in diet, or poor nutrition, but can also be due to an unchecked invasion of parasites, such as Red Mite. They could also be viral or bacterial infections and if the other causes are ruled out you should consult your vet.

Aspergillosis

This lung disease is preventable as it is caused by a fungus which builds up in damp conditions. Bark chippings are discussed in the Housing chapter and are prone to a build up of the fungus. A fungus outbreak can also occur in the hen house floor covering if it is not cleaned regularly. A spilt or leaking drinker, as well as old food lying around can provide ideal conditions for the fungus. Thus, good management will easily prevent any outbreak. The disease causes a rattly breathing noise in an infected bird, which will stretch out its neck to breathe easier. Death usually occurs within 24 hours. There is no treatment, so prevention is better than cure.

Blackhead

This is more associated with turkeys than chickens, but nevertheless can still occur. An affected hen will be listless and go off her food. She will suffer rapid weight loss and will often have bright yellow diarrhoea. The disease is caused by a parasite which is spread by a roundworm which sets up residence in the caecal tracts and liver. If untreated, the hen will die of blood poisoning, due to peritonitis. Treatment is simple by putting Dimetridazole (available from an agricultural supplier) in the drinking water. Within 24 hours the hen will pick up and begin eating again. The problem with Blackhead is that it gets into the soil from the droppings of an infected hen and can remain there for years. There is no clear up possible and that part of land should not be used for chickens or turkeys again.

Blood Spots On The Shell

Most common cause is a rupture of blood capillaries in the oviduct which become part of the shell as it is made. This can be caused by a vitamin A deficiency. An increase in blood spots is associated with Fowl Cholera, but this is not a common disease. If it is suspected, you should contact your vet.

Blood spots on the shell can also be caused by red mite moving into the hen house. They live in the crevices of the hen house and feed on the hens at night. See the Red Mite section in Troubleshooting for how to deal with them. The faeces of the Red Mite can cause black spots on the shell and such spots are another pointer to Red Mite infestation.

Broodiness

For the purposes of this book, written for the Chicken Keeper relying on eggs, broodiness is a nuisance. A broody hen will always choose the most popular nest box and make herself comfortable, emitting a high pitched long shriek if another hen tries to climb in on top of her. The other hens become agitated at not being able to use the nest box and eggs are laid elsewhere, generally causing chaos all round. The best cure is to remove her to a place on her own and hope that the appeal of sitting all on her own will wear off. It may take a couple of days.

If she is removed from the main flock, it is important to keep her in view of the rest of the flock to keep her part of the community. If she is out of sight for a period of time, she may be a stranger on her return and subjected to the bullying a newcomer receives. An old rabbit cage, or something similar, placed in the run with her isolated inside should soon change her mind.

Change In Egg Colour

Strong sunshine beating down on hens that cannot shelter in shade can result in lighter brown eggs than usual. An associated problem of warm drinking water can have the same effect. If a change in egg colour happens during a sunny period these are the most likely causes. There are four pigments for the particular mix of pigment that the hen uses for her usual colour of egg. The lack of one or more of the pigments due to the hen reducing the amount of food she is eating will change the colour of her egg. The reduction could be due to insufficient food being supplied, or a change in food to one which does not contain the required pigmentation.

A change in egg colour can also indicate Red Mite and the henhouse should be checked as a precaution.

Coccidiosis

An affected hen will stand around listless and hunched up. She will have milky white diarrhoea, sometimes with blood in it. The hen will also be very thirsty. It affects birds of all ages, but young birds are most vulnerable. It is treatable, but has to be spotted early as it causes sudden death. It is caused by a protozoan parasite which lives in the small intestine, duodenum and caecal tracts. The parasite eggs are passed out of the hen in the droppings and like warm, wet conditions to develop. Good hygiene on the hen house floor will help prevent spread of this and this and Aspergillosis (above). It is treated with Baytox which is available from a vet. See also the section on coccidiosis under Runny Poo.

Common Cold

Yes, even chickens can catch the common cold. The only symptom is a slimy, runny nose, often blowing bubbles in one nostril. There is no smell around the beak and the eyes are not swollen. The hen appears perfectly happy in herself.

Hens can catch a cold in damp, draughty conditions in the same way we can. A sudden change in temperature can also give them a cold. There are cures available, but it usually clears up on its own.

Crop

Impacted

A hen will hold an amount of grit and crushed oyster shell in her crop. There is also a small quantity of grit in her stomach. The hen will fill up with food in the morning, graze throughout the day and fill up again with corn or wheat in the evening. The food first goes into the crop and then is slowly released from the crop unto the stomach. Once the crop is full the hen will need to stop eating for a while until there is space in the crop to allow her to eat again. It is a continuous process, so more often than not the crop will be full. By the same token, it will be rare for the crop to be empty.

So, firstly, if an impacted crop is suspected the crop will have to have been full for a while and the hen will not have eaten for a while. If the hen is being given a balanced diet of layers pellets and/or mash in the morning and corn or wheat in the evening, crop impaction should not occur. It is sticky scraps, such as bread and pasta, or stringy vegetables such as celery and cabbage, even long grass, that can cause a problem. This is another reason not to feed any scraps at all. If you are sure the crop is impacted, a spoonful of olive oil and massage may help. There are two schools of thought on the direction in which to encourage the impaction to leave. One suggests holding the hen upside down by her feet and massaging the impaction out of her beak and the other suggests encouraging the contents of the crop to follow the normal path into the stomach.

If the food has been stuck for a while this can start to rot and lead to sour crop. If this has happened, mix some potassium permanganate in water, just enough to turn it light purple. Use a dropper to get as much in as possible and massage the impaction out of her beak whilst holding her upside down.

If all this fails, then it is a trip to the vet, who will remove the impaction by making a slit over the crop, sliding the impaction out and stitching up.

Empty

If you have occasion to pick a hen up, just feel her crop gently. The crop is at the base of her neck, where it joins her chest. As described above, a hen on a healthy diet should always have something in it. If it is empty this is unusual and will require investigation. The obvious answer is that she isn't feeding for some reason. Is her beak free of obstruction? Is enough food being left out for all of them? Is she being bullied off the food station? It is often a good idea to split the feed stations and have two. A bully will have her work cut out running between the two if she has decided to pick on a particular hen. She will soon forget her mission to bully when she gets carried away in feeding herself instead. In practical terms, if you have a number of hens, two stations will offer twice as much area for the chickens to gather around.

Egg Bound

This is where an egg has got stuck due to the muscles around the vent contracting and not letting the egg out. A suffering hen will be trying to push the egg out with no luck. Sometimes the tip of the egg can be seen. If a little olive oil rubbed around the vent doesn't help, the problem will be solved with warmth. If you can, try warming her vent with a hair dryer set on low heat. Alternatively put the hen in a box with holes in the base and with shavings or straw on the bottom. Put the box containing the hen on a source of heat, such as a radiator, and let nature take its course. The egg should be produced in a few hours. Another variation on the heat theme is to hold the hen **securely** over a pan of boiling water to allow the steam to relax the vent. Hold her high enough over the water to allow the steam to get to her, but not to scald her!

If all else fails and the egg can be seen, puncture the visible part and use your fingers to get the shell and contents out. Be very sure you have got it all out as any remains can cause an infection.

If the egg is higher up in the oviduct and not stuck because of a cramp in the vent muscles there is nothing you can do and the hen will die.

Egg Drop Syndrome (EDS)

This virus affects the reproductive system and has an incubation period of 7 to 17 days. It is not fatal. It occurs in mature hens, often in brown-egg layers. There is a gradual drop in laying, resulting in about half the normal quantity of eggs. The virus progresses slowly and an attack can last from 4 to 10 weeks. The eggs can have pale shells, thin gritty shells, soft shells or no shells at all. The symptoms are unique to this syndrome in the hen does not appear to be unwell at all.

The virus is primarily carried by ducks and geese. They are only a carrier and the virus does not affect them at all. Transmission is by contact with infected waterfowl or surface water contaminated by them, or contact with the droppings of an infected chicken.

There is no treatment, except to isolate the affected bird to prevent it spreading to the rest of the flock. The hen should recover within a 10 week period.

Egg Eating

Egg eating is a habit to be quickly stopped as it can become permanent. Hens are not predisposed to egg eating, so if it has started it has done so for a reason. It will usually be due to a lack of something in a hen's diet. This can be lack of cool water as well as lack of food. It started in my flock in a heat wave. There was water left in the drinkers in the evening, so I was not alerted to the water crisis. Once the egg eating started I added another drinker in the pen and it stopped as fast as it had started.

Eggs Smell And Taste Fishy

Can be caused by one of many reasons

- Fish taint obtained by storage near fish products

- Some plants, if eaten by a layer, can give a taint to the eggs. These include, garlic, oilseed rape and wild onion.

- Too much fishmeal in the layers pellets or mash.

- Fish oil has recently been added to some poultry feeds to increase the Omega 3 value of the eggs. An antioxidant, such as Vitamin E is also added to counteract the fishy effect of the oil and sometimes the balance may not be right.

- Flax seeds, canola and Soya beans are also sources of Omega 3. Too much flaxseed can darken the yolks and leave them with a fishy taste.

- If you encounter a fishy taste problem, try changing the food you are giving your hens. If that works it is worth comparing the ingredients of the two feeds and contacting the manufacturer of the offending food.

Feather Loss

A hen can suddenly appear with feathers pulled out, often on her wings. Feather pecking and aggression most often happens when there are too many hens being kept in the space available. The only solution in this case is to reduce the number of hens or increase the area available. It is accepted that a hen can recognise a maximum of 50 other hens. In a flock larger than 50, recognition will become a problem and aggression will follow as an unrecognised hen will become a 'stranger' and open to attack.

There are, however, some breeds of hen which are just aggressive. The hybrids have had this tendency bred out of them, but it is worth checking this aspect if considering a traditional breed.

Lack of nutrients in the diet can also lead to feather pecking. Feathers have a blood content and so are nutritious. Check that enough layers pellets and/or mash is being provided. Poultry spice and/or kelp seaweed powder will help the pecked hen re-grow her feathers quickly.

Once feather pecking has started it will become a vice. Even after the original trigger has been rectified feather pecking can continue. There are various tricks to employ to discourage this behaviour. You can get a product to paint on the victim that tastes horrible and discourages the attacker, much like the horrible tasting nail varnish used to discourage nail biting children. Try removing the victim for a few days and see if the perpetrator starts on someone else. If they do, then remove them instead for a few days. The pecking order will have changed on her return and will make bullying more difficult.

Hens can often develop a bald back. If this happens, it is almost certainly due to the attentions of a cockerel. This is the second most popular reason, after the noise factor, for not keeping a cockerel. The mating action of almost running on the spot on her back, known as treading, can result in severe feather loss. This can be especially so in the case of soft feathered birds, such as Buff Orpingtons. The obvious answer is to only keep a cockerel if you intend to breed from him and to keep him in a separate pen until his services are required for fertile eggs. If the flock is large enough his attentions will be widely spread and so no one hen should suffer from feather loss through treading, but is unfair on a few hens for them to bear the constant attention of a cockerel. One answer is to put a cloth saddle on the hen to protect her back. Saddles are not sold in most shops, but are available on the Internet. They are easy to fit, but check under them regularly as it is easy for lice to set up home underneath them.

Floor Laid Eggs

If this is a regular occurrence this will indicate a reluctance to go into the nest box. It could be that the boxes are not easily accessible, in which case a rail for them to jump onto first before stepping into the nest box will help. If you have a number of hens there may not be enough nest boxes, in which case the provision of a few more will quickly solve the problem. It may be that the nest boxes are too open or dirty. Hens like a clean, dark area in which to lay in comfort. Another cause may be an infestation of Lice or Red Mite in the nest box and it is worth keeping a regular eye on this. I would recommend shaking some lice powder into the nest box flooring when you put a fresh lot in, as the hen will benefit from getting a dose of it when she settles down in the nest box to lay.

If there is the odd floor laid egg, don't worry. I often come across one in the food room, or by the log pile. I can picture a hen too busy eating and looking around in surprise as an egg appears! Sometimes they just seem to be too busy to make it to the nest box in time.

Fowl Pest

This is a rare disease now, but is still possible. It usually takes hold in a heat wave when the hens become stressed with the heat. An infected hen will sit hunched up and have a discharge from the nostrils. They will have watery green or white diarrhoea and can die quickly in the severe form of the disease. In less severe cases death is not certain, but the hens have difficulty breathing and their heads can look swollen. It is caused by a bacterium and is highly contagious. It can be spread by wild birds, vermin, people, water, equipment, and vehicles, virtually anything. It is a notifiable disease and infected birds will be culled. There in no prevention, only good hygiene if an outbreak is reported in your area.

Frostbite

There is always the danger of a sharp frost during the winter months, which sometimes even takes the forecasters by surprise. Birds with large combs and wattles can be prone to frostbite and special attention need to be paid to them in a cold snap. Make sure the hen house is draught free and do not let the hens out too early. The combs can be protected with a coating of Vaseline. If they have been affected by frostbite, the affected part will not recover and may need to be trimmed by a vet.

Infectious Bronchitis

A hen with I.B. will be gasping for breath and make a rattling sound as she does. In a laying bird there will be drop in egg production, with eggs being produced misshapen and with poor quality shells. The eggs can have a rough texture and can suffer a loss of pigmentation, especially in brown eggs. The egg white will appear watery and the yolk will slide about instead of being held in place. I. B. is spread by a virus which can pass from hen to hen on her breath, but can also spread on equipment and clothing. There is no treatment other than good hygiene for equipment and a hen will usually recover. However, her fallopian tubes will be damaged and she will continue to lay misshapen eggs. For this reason infected birds are usually culled. It is easily prevented by vaccination.

Lice

Fowl lice live on the hen and will be by the hens pecking and scratching themselves as the lice tickle them. There are at least six different types of lice and each type prefers a different part of the hen's body. The lice live on the skin and lay their eggs on the feather shafts. The eggs are called nits, making fowl lice much the same as human hair lice. Fowl lice reproduce very quickly and the powders treat the lice, but not the nits. Treatment must be repeated in 10 days time in order to catch the newly hatched lice and break the cycle.

Prevention is definitely the watch word in dealing with lice. I dust my chickens with louse powder when they arrive and would suggest you do the same. Sprinkle louse powder in the nest boxes when you clean them out and in their dust bath in the summer, when it is dust and not mud!

Mareks Disease

This is also known as Fowl Paralysis, although the birds are not always paralysed. It affects birds between the ages of 6 to 20 weeks. One a hen reaches laying age she appears to have built up immunity, but can still transmit the disease. There are two forms of the disease; the classical, which affects the legs and wings and acute, which affects various organs such as heart, liver, kidneys, lungs or spleen and always ends in the death of the hen. The classical form of the disease will not always cause death, but culling of the affected hen is the kinder option. Because of the two forms there are a number of symptoms, but not all may be present and Mareks disease may even only be diagnosed with a post mortem after a mysterious death. A classic symptom is outstretched legs, often with one in front and one behind. They are unable to walk or can hobble using a wing as a crutch. They can simply just look off colour and not be growing. Alternatively, they can be ravenously hungry, but still very thin. Sometimes they hold their beaks open in a gape.

The disease is caused by the herpes virus and is spread by feather dust being inhaled by a chick or grower. It has a long incubation time which means you can buy apparently healthy chicks which die in horrible circumstances a few weeks later.

If you have suffered an outbreak of Mareks Disease the hen house and all equipment must be disinfected with Virkon, available from pet shops, before restocking.

The disease is easily preventable by vaccination and the hens I sell are all vaccinated by my supplier.

Mycoplasma

This covers mycoplasmosis, coryza, colds, Infectious Synovitis, Infectious sinusitis, Roup which are all different diseases, but have similar symptoms and the same treatment.

The obvious signs are a discharge from the nose and bubbles in the corner of the eyes. This leads to the bird scratching the eye area and wiping her infected eye on the base of her neck, so leaving a mark on her feathers. She will start sneezing and making a rattling noise, but the most distinctive is a dreadful smell from her nostrils. If left untreated, one or both eyes will swell enough to close the infected eye and she may even lose her sight. A telltale sign in the beginning is a sticky substance on the hen's shoulder where she has leant

over and rubbed her sore eye. With Infectious Synovitis the hock joints swell making walking difficult.

The diseases are spread by sneezing and in the drinking water. Clean drinking water daily is a must. The diseases can be treated with antibiotics from your vet, but can only suppress them, allowing them to reappear later. They are not fatal diseases in themselves, but it is usually better to cull an infected bird because of the difficulty if ridding the flock of the diseases.

If you smell a dreadful smell on the nostril of a bird you are buying, do not buy it at it certainly has Mycoplasma.

Red Mite

Red Mites have eight legs and are therefore a member of the spider family. They are probably introduced to the hen house by wild birds. They live in the crevices and joints of the hen house and particularly like the comfort of roof felt. They don't like light and hide away during the day. They like an easy life and will inhabit the nearest crevices to the perch so they have the least distance to travel. The first place to check for Red Mite is at the end of the perch and a removable perch will make eradication easier. They come out at night when the hens are in the hen house roosting and drink their fill of blood from the hens. There are no real hints of red mite on the hens except that they can look anaemic, with pale faces and combs, if they have been under sustained attack. The main clue is reluctance on the part of the hens to enter the hen house at night. They are creatures of habit and can become frantic if they are unable to go to bed at night, if the door has blown closed in the wind, for example.

Reluctance to go in means the problem is serious. Colonies of red mite are easy to spot if you look for them. They look like a cluster of red dots and it is worth checking each time you clean the hen house out, or weekly if the cleaning interval is longer. They are more prevalent in summer, but can hit at any time. Another clue is an outbreak of a whitish dust on the perches or falling from the roof when you reach into the hen house. This is the skin shells of the mite, cast off as they grow.

In the above photo of Red Mite caught in my hen house, a section of loose bark has been pulled back to reveal a thriving colony underneath. Immediately after the photo was taken they were quickly killed with the blow torch.

Eradication is achieved by dismantling the hen house as far as possible and spraying with a Red Mite spray. There are a number of them on the market, but I prefer Breckasol, which is made entirely from garlic. The ultimate remover, in my view, is the blow torch. Red Mite can become tolerant to some insecticides and can scarper as they see the spray coming towards them. They bury themselves deep in the cracks, only to emerge unscathed when the spray has passed. If you do decide to use an insecticidal spray, use a variety of the as the Mite can develop a resistance if the same one is used over a period of time. Obvious care has to be taken when using a blow torch and make sure there are no areas left smouldering. The Mites disintegrate with a snap, crackle and pop, which is very satisfying. Treatments will have to be repeated, often a number of times in order to break the lifecycle of the Red Mite.

Another practical and satisfying method of controlling Red Mite, especially if you have no other method on hand, is to wrap Sellotape around each end of the perch so that the sticky side is on the outside. In the morning there will be a satisfying catch of Mite all stuck fast to the tape. It has the added advantage that the hens will have been protected as the Mite will not have been able to get to them.

If the infestation is such that treatments are not eradicating them it may be better to destroy the perches or other offending item and start again. It is not satisfactory to put the infested item in the bin and certainly not on the compost heap. The best method is incineration.

Roosting Outside

Often in the height of summer the Jungle Fowl instincts are awakened and the hens will take to perching in the trees or on fence tops at bedtime, instead of tucking themselves safely into the hen house. If their new roosting spot really is fox proof then leave them to it. If they choose a tree outside the pen, don't panic as they will drop back into the pen in the morning. If there is any danger of fox attack at all, the hens must be discouraged from this new found freedom. Supervising bedtime can help; if you are on hand you can shoo them into the hen house before they have set off on heir route up the tree. Throwing a handful of grain into the house will often be all the encouragement they need. If they have already made it up to their new perch, then it may be a case of getting a

stepladder out. Grab their feet, rather than their body as it can be done with one hand and gives better control of a struggling bird.

Jungle Fowl instinct should not be confused with a reluctance to go into the hen house. Any sign of reluctance at all could indicate the presence of Red Mite and it is still worth checking the house for Mite even if Jungle Fowl instincts are all that is suspected.

Runny Poo

I find that a number of hens do not produce the classic brown solid poo with a white top. It can often be a lot softer. The main point is to be aware of any change from the norm. The table below lists the common diseases and the diarrhoea symptoms. If you suspect any of these, consult your vet. Loose, watery droppings are a cooling mechanism in hot weather and so nothing to worry about in a heat wave.

Disease	Symptom
Campylobacteriosis	Bloody diarrhoea
Chronic Respiratory Disease	Yellowish poo, not necessarily runny
Colibacillosis	Yellow, watery, foamy diarrhoea
Coccidiosis	Watery, light brown or bloody diarrhoea; can contain mucus
Lymphoid leukosis	Loose white or green poo
Tuberculosis	Persistent diarrhoea, usually in older hens
Worms	Foamy diarrhoea

Campylobacteriosis is an intestinal disease which can affect humans as well as chickens. The main symptoms are lethargy and diarrhoea as described in the table. There is no known cure and culling may be necessary. A vet should confirm the diagnosis before a decision is taken. The hen house and run should be thoroughly cleansed and disinfected, then left empty to dry out completely for at least a week before introducing new birds.

Chronic Respiratory Disease - see Mycoplasmosis.

Colibacillosis is a group of infectious diseases caused by E.coli. The bacteria could act alone, or combine with other diseases, such as chronic respiratory disease, infectious bronchitis and Newcastle's Disease. It affects younger birds more than older ones.

The bacteria can survive for long periods in dry litter. It enters the hen by being eaten or breathed in and is spread through the droppings of infected rodents and chickens. If it gets into the bloodstream it will cause sudden death.

It can be treated with the antibiotic Terramycin 5% administered in the drinking water. Eggs should be thrown away for 7 days after the dose is administered.

Coccidiosis is a disease caused by coccidian parasites, which are found in the intestines of most chickens. As the hen gets older she develops on immunity, but it can kill young chicks. The coccidian irritate the intestinal lining, making it more difficult for the lining to absorb the nutrition from the food. It is spread by a chicken eating food contaminated by the droppings of an infected bird. Good food hygiene will help prevention. A vet will be able to analyse a sample of dropping and tell you whether the infection is an internal parasite as in coccidiosis, or a bacteria, such as colibacillosis.

Coccidiosis is treated with Baycox, administered in water. Use a specified on the packaging and be sure to destroy the eggs for the required period.

Lymphoid leukosis is a viral infection and is fatal. It will be identified by post mortem as death can be very quick.

Tuberculosis is a disease which requires a long period of exposure and so mainly affects older birds. It is not lethal, but causes lethargy and loss of weight. There is no cure and the culling of an infected bird is essential to prevent spread. It is also very difficult to decontaminate the area and so the area should not house chickens in the future. A new flock in a new area is the best way to eradicate the disease.

Worms are easily detected by the presence of foamy diarrhoea. Other symptoms Are: pale, anaemic head, lethargy, reduction in egg production and a gradual weight loss. Only use a wormer if you have to, if the hens are losing weight and egg production has stopped. I recommend Flubenvet, although there are others available. Flubenvet was withdrawn from sale in early 2006 due to a European Directive. It has been realised that the withdrawal of Flubenvet has caused problems for small flock keepers and so a dispensation from the Directive has been organised, resulting in it being available again. Carefully follow the dosage instructions and be sure to destroy the eggs for the required period after administering a dose if advised to do to on the packaging.

Scaley Leg

Scaley leg is caused by a mite which takes up residence under the scales of a hen's leg. The scales become lifted as the mites ease their way in. The lifted scales are the first sign of an infestation and then the legs will start to swell because of the irritation of the mite. The cure is to hold each leg in turn in a jar of surgical spirit once a week for four weeks. Hold it up to the hock joint for 20 seconds each time. The hen may flinch when you do this. This is because the surgical

spirit is cold, not because of any discomfort. Be careful not to knock any scales off her legs as they may bleed and scales are only replaced annually.

Yolkless egg

A yolkless egg happens when the yolk has missed the funnel opening to the oviduct and landed in the abdomen. The egg is perfect in every other way, but egg peritonitis in a hen is caused by yolks in the wrong place in her body. If a hen looks off colour after a yolkless egg has turned up contact your vet for antibiotics without delay.

Eggs

10

The subject of eggs almost merits a book in its own right. Eggs really are fascinating. This chapter explores the history of eggs and egg games together with how an egg is formed and the contents of an egg. How many calories in an egg? Read on to find out.

Traditions And Superstitions Associated With Eggs

In ancient mythology the egg was the symbol of the creation of the world and also symbolized life and death to almost every civilization through the centuries. Pagans were said to celebrate the arrival of spring by walking to a 'magic tree' in the village. The children gave each other coloured hard boiled eggs. A great feast followed and the villagers gave thanks to the goddess Eostre for bringing the land back to life.

The ancient Persian and Celtic cultures celebrated the spring equinox with the gift of red dyed eggs. The eggs were shared at a meal and afterwards the shells were carefully crushed in a ritual to drive away winter. Another custom, which is believed to have originated in Germany, is to hang red dyed eggs in evergreen trees as a powerful symbol of rebirth and renewal.

The custom of decorating eggs is very old. The ban of eating eggs during the 46 days of Lent was established in the 9th century and is what made eggs so popular at Easter. The eggs were collected and saved and, once the fasting was over, were distributed to the servants and children often in a huge Easter omelette. By the 13th century in England, it had become customary to give gifts of coloured hard boiled eggs on Easter Sunday. It was common to use plant dyes and other natural substances to decorate the eggs in a rainbow of colours. As the practice became more refined, it moved up to the nobility who used the last days of winter to decorate eggs to give to their loved one, their master, or the King. The household accounts of Edward1 for 1290 record that 450 eggs were purchased for 1/6d (7p) which were to be covered with leaf gold or stained by boiling and distributed to members of the Royal Household.

By the 16th century, these springtime eggs were the height of fashion at the French Court, with some nobles employing the greatest artists of the day to paint decorated eggs. The popularity of the Easter egg reached ultimate heights at the Court of the Czar of Russia. By the end of the 19th century, the court jeweller, Carl Faberge, was making fabulous jewel encrusted eggs of gold or porcelain. Today, hand-decorated eggs are exchanged at springtime in many cultures and play an important role in religious ceremonies on Easter Sunday. Some families carefully save their egg collection, passing them on from generation to generation.

In England there was a tradition for families to take large baskets of hard boiled eggs to the local church to be blessed on Easter Sunday. These 'holy' eggs would be carried home and placed as the table centrepiece, surrounded by large platters of meat. In wealthy homes the best tableware was used to honour the 'Easter Eggs'. Sometimes the centrepiece eggs were decorated to form a colourful display which was kept throughout Easter week. Visitors to the house were invited to eat one of the eggs to break the Lenten fast, during which the eating of eggs had been forbidden. Pancakes were traditionally made on Shrove Tuesday to use up the eggs prior to the Lenten fast, a tradition which continues today.

There are a number of superstitions associated with eggs laid during Easter.

Eggs laid on Good Friday will stay fresh indefinitely.

Eggs laid on Good Friday or Easter Sunday and eaten on the same day were believed to bring good fortune to the lucky consumer.

Eggs laid on Good Friday or Easter Sunday were used in folk medicine to cure ailments and were said to protect against fever the whole year through. Thrown into the heart of a fire they were thought to have the power to extinguish the blaze. Buried in the ground or on the edge of a field they were believed to guard against lightening and hail as well as protecting beehives.

Easter Egg Games

Easter Egg Hunt

There are a number of traditional Easter egg games, some of which are still played today. The best known is probably the Easter egg hunt. Eggs, most usually chocolate ones, are hidden around the house or garden and the children have a wonderful time finding and eating them. If chocolate overload is a worry, then a substitute can be hidden, such as coloured ping pong balls, which can then be exchanged for a treat at the end. Our children's primary school organizes one each year for the whole school of about 100 children, which is thoroughly enjoyed by all. There is a village in America where one family organizes an Easter Egg hunt for the entire village. They use around 2,000 plastic refillable eggs and seem to fill them around the year! Whatever scale you choose to play it on, it is Easter fun for all the family.

Here a few rules which may help.

- Keep a count of how many eggs have been hidden and how many are found. It saves a molten chocolate shock some time later.

- Hide them away from pets. Human chocolate can be dangerous for pets, which don't seem to appreciate the danger.

- Hide them in easy as well as difficult places, to appeal to all ages.

- Let young children have a head start.

- Hide some spot prize eggs for a special treat.

Egg Rolling

This game requires some sort of gentle slope, even a gentle undulation in the lawn. The contestants first have fun personalizing hard boiled eggs. When the eggs are decorated to the satisfaction of their owners the game is ready to be played. Each contestant rolls their eggs in turn and the winner is the one to have travelled the furthest, or suffered the least damage. They can, of course, all be rolled at once, with the winner being decided as before. The most famous version of this is the annual White House Easter Egg Roll on the front lawn. Alternatively, there is an old French custom where raw eggs, marked to identify the owner, are rolled down a gentle slope. The egg that survives the roll and attacks by competing eggs is declared the 'victory egg'. Whatever version of the game, it is said to represent the rock which rolled away from the tomb when Jesus rose from the dead.

Egg Tapping

This game is similar to conkers in that the egg shell to suffer the least damage wins. Using hard boiled eggs, each contestant holds their egg in a clenched fist with just the round end showing slightly. They then take it in turns to strike the top of their opponent's egg with their own. The eggs are then turned over to reveal the pointy end and the process of hitting each other is continued. The winner, as stated before, is the one with the least damage.

Egg Throwing

This game is attributed to parts of Denmark, Switzerland and Germany. The egg is thrown from one contestant to the next, standing in a circle a fixed distance from each other. The egg must be caught intact, or the contestant is disqualified. When it has gone around once the successful contestants move back a few paces and the egg is thrown from one to the next again. The process is repeated until there is a winner. The description I read did not specify whether the egg was fresh or hard boiled. It seems to me that it can be decided by the players and dictated by the number of fresh eggs available.

Egg Bowling

As with most of these games, the hard boiled eggs are decorated, with the exception of one to be used as the target egg. It helps to have a white egg, or alternatively, one could be painted plain white. The target egg is placed in the arena and each player bowls his decorated egg. The winner is the painted egg closest to the white egg without touching it and, crucially, without moving it.

Egg Decorating

For short term use the egg can be hard boiled, but the best egg to use is one where the contents have been removed. These are known as blown eggs, because the contents have been blown out. It is easy to do; it just requires a thick sewing needle and a lot of puff.

Carefully prick both ends of the egg. Then push most of the needle in to the shell and swirl it around to puncture the yolk sac. Next, holding the egg over a bowl, blow the contents out. Duck, goose or even ostrich eggs are ideal if you need something bigger than a hen's egg.

Once you have your prepared egg shell there is no limit to the designs. Try tying some ribbon around a decorated egg and hanging a number of them off a sprig of forsythia or pussy willow for a striking decoration. Wedge the twig into a decorated plant pot for the ultimate finish. See the egg decorating section in the Children's chapter for more ideas.

How An Egg Is Formed

Eggs come in all shapes, colours and sizes, but are made in the same way and have the same contents.

A pullet between 18–22 weeks of age is known as point of lay because it is at this time that the ovaries will start producing egg follicles. The follicles are the first stage in the production of the egg.

Chickens have two ovaries, but only the left one will produce follicles. They start as little tiny yolks (follicles) and ripen on the ovary until they are released. At any one time there are a number of follicles ripening on the ovary. The time taken for ripening will depend on a number of factors, such as the different seasons. Hybrid hens will produce a ripe yolk virtually every day because they have been bred to achieve this. Pure breed hens will take a bit longer to produce a ripe yolk and therefore tend to lay fewer eggs per year than a hybrid hen.

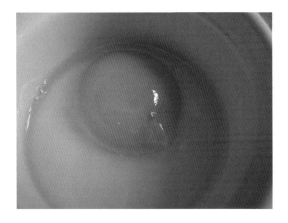

The oviduct of a laying hen is about 60–75 cm long and consists of five parts. These are: the funnel opening to the oviduct (ifundibulum), the section producing the albumen, the section where the membranes are formed, the section where the shell is formed and the vagina/cloaca which pushes out the finished egg. When ripe, the follicle will detach itself from the ovary and drop into the oviduct through the funnel opening. If two are released at the same time it will result in a double yolked egg. Once in the oviduct the follicle becomes the yolk of the egg and is thickened, which takes about 15 minutes. The thickened yolk then moves to the next part of the oviduct where half the

albumen is formed. This stage takes about three hours. The chalazae is also made here which is the stringy substance, much like hammock ties, which keeps the yolk in position inside the egg. In the next stage of production the two membranes are formed. One membrane encloses the egg contents and the other will stick to the inside of the shell. If you imagine peeling a boiled egg, the shell is held together by a thin, but strong, skin and there is a separate skin around the hard contents. Next the second half of the albumen is added and the shell contents are complete. The construction of the shell takes about 20 hours and once the shell is on, the egg is ready to be laid. Thus a hen will lay an egg every 25 to 30 hours depending on the breed.

The eggshell is made predominantly of pure calcium with small amounts of phosphorous, magnesium, manganese and some albumen. The albumen, which is coated on the shell just before the egg is laid, acts as glue binding the eggshell together. The albumen forms a very thin layer on the outside of the shell, known as the bloom. The eggshell is not the same thickness all over. It is thicker on the pointed end and thinner at the sides.

An eggshell has thousands of small holes, called pores. Pores are important for the exchanges of gases and moisture during incubation and hatching. There is an average of 7,500 pores on a shell and most of them are at the large rounded end. Whilst their primary aim is to assist the development of

the chick, they also have an effect on an unfertilized egg in that strong odours can enter the egg through the pores and give the egg a 'taste', which is why eggs should be stored from strong smelling substances. By the same token, moisture is lost through the pores and I will come onto this when discussing the freshness of an egg. The air cell of an egg is at the large rounded end and most of the pores of an egg are also at this end. Immediately after the shell is formed in the hen the air cell is formed between the membrane around the egg white and the membrane on the inside of the shell.

If the egg passes a little slower than normal through the shell coating section in the oviduct, the shell can have a wrinkled effect. If a complete stoppage takes place there the egg in progress can be caught up by the next one in line. When this happens, both eggs can get coated with the shell by the shell gland even though the first one has already got one. This will result in a larger egg with the surprise of an egg within an egg. Although unusual, such a stoppage can occur for a number of reasons, but usually where the hen has had a fright. When frightened, she reacts to the fright by temporarily freezing until the frightening episode has passed. A hen can be frightened by anything out of the ordinary, such as a barking dog, passing bird of prey, noisy helicopter or aeroplane etc.

On the other hand, occasionally a soft-shell egg may turn up, and is nothing to worry about. It is simply where the egg has missed the shell formation section for some reason. It can often happen when a pullet first comes into lay. However, if it is a regular event then you should consult a vet, as it is a symptom of Egg Drop Syndrome, Influenza, Infectious Bronchitis, and Infectious Laryngotracheitis. As the names imply, these conditions are infectious, so quick diagnosis is essential. I stress, though, that these conditions may only be present if a soft-shell egg is a regular occurrence and is unlikely to occur in inoculated birds. The lack of vitamin D in the hen's diet could be the most likely cause and is easily rectified. The hen absorbs vitamin D naturally through sunlight, but where there are consistently short days with little or no sunlight, cod

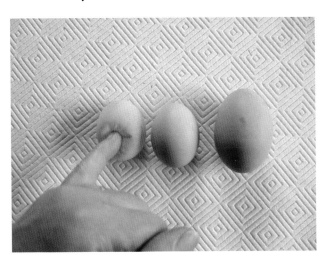

liver oil will provide vitamin D. See also the Egg Drop Syndrome section in Troubleshooting.

All sorts of odd things can happen in the egg production process, such as this egg, where it has been given an outer covering of thick membrane.

In the past the corner shop would have sold an odd shaped egg and no-one would have thought twice. Now that we have rules and regulations on the perfection of our produce we no longer see such oddities. Needless to say, the contents are all the same, no matter what the shell looks like!

Very occasionally an egg can turn up without a yolk. If you look at the funnel at the beginning of the oviduct, you can see that it would be possible for a yolk to miss the entrance. If it does, it will land in the abdomen. Egg peritonitis is caused by yolks in the wrong place, so if a hen looks ill after an egg has turned up without a yolk, contact your vet for antibiotics immediately. Yolkless eggs can be laid by a very young pullet at the beginning of lay, or an old hen at the end of lay. Neither of these are a cause for concern.

Yolk colour is determined by the amount of xanthophylls and carotenoid pigments in the plants they eat. They are not able to make the pigments themselves and so have to get them from their diet. If they

Egg showing blood spots in the shell

did not, the yolks would be colourless. Some layers mash and pellets contain yolk colour enhancer to supplement the diet. Yolk colour is measured on the Roche Scale. The average free-range hen in Spring and Summer has eggs with a yolk colour of 8–9 on the scale. In winter this reduces down to 4–5. Yolk colour has

118

no connection with the nutritional value of an egg. Eggs can even have green yolks, which are caused by the hen eating acorns or shepherd's purse.

Eggshell colour is mainly hereditary. It is controlled by the cockerel, so the son of a dark egg laying hen, for example, will pass the trait onto his daughters. The breeding of hybrid hens bred for eggshell colour will take this into account. As stated above, the pigmentation in the shell is added during the shell formation stage. There are four pigments that may be added and each breed of hen has a distinctive mix of them. A total lack of pigment will produce a white egg. There is no link between the colour of the shell and the contents of the egg. The eggshell colour may also be affected by the general health of the hen, her food and even the weather conditions. Any one of these can slightly change the colour of her egg. A change in colour of egg from the same chicken, usually the loss of dark pigment in eggs usually laid by a dark brown egg layer, can be caused by various factors. It happens more often in summer due to strong sunshine beating down on the hens and/or their drinking water becoming warm. Care must be taken to provide shade for the hens and their drinkers. If the hen reduces the amount of food she is eating, or the food is changed to one without the necessary pigments, the colour of the egg will become lighter. An unexplained change in egg colour may indicate an infection and a vet should be consulted.

I have attached three schedules at the end of this chapter showing the colour of egg laid by each breed of hen. Two schedules link the egg colour desired to the hen required, the other lists the breed of hen and the colour of the egg they produce. It is interesting to note that there are far more traditional breeds which lay white eggs than brown ones. There can occasionally be tiny blood spots in the shell. The most common cause is a rupture of small blood capillaries in the oviduct which become part of the shell as it passes through. There is some evidence that this trait is hereditary and a hen regularly producing such eggs should not be used for breeding. The hybrid varieties of chicken, such as the Black Rock, have had this taken into account, so it is rare occurrence with them. An occasional egg with blood spots may be due to a Vitamin A deficiency. However, an increase in blood spots is associated with Fowl Cholera, which should be treated by a vet. This is a very rare disease and blood spots are most likely to be hereditary or a Vitamin A deficiency as described above.

Egg Laying

Your chickens will not always lay in their nest boxes and you may have to go on you own egg hunt. A good indication of this happening is when you believe that your hen has stopped laying. She may have, but then she may be laying somewhere else. These photos are from my very early days of chicken

keeping. After a week of no eggs I went hunting!

A hen will 'announce' that she has laid an egg. This goes back to flock days in the wild when a cockerel looked after his flock of young ladies. A hen will have been aware of her environment when she left the flock to lay an egg in the hedgerow, but she may have been in there a little while and circumstances may have changed. She 'announces' that she has laid her egg in order to call the cockerel over to escort her safely back to the flock.

The number of eggs a hen will lay will depend largely on breed and breeding. Breeding is important because a renowned good laying breed, such as the Rhode Island Red, will inherit her prolific egg laying quality from her father. If an inferior cockerel is used in breeding, his daughters will not lay as well as they should. It is for this reason that the breeding of Black Rocks is very strictly controlled by one producer in Scotland. The careful selection of breeding birds and the insistence on always using the first cross between a

120

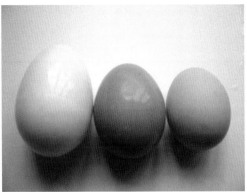

The large white egg has a double yolk

Rhode Island Red cockerel and a Plymouth Rock hen consistently produces Black Rock progeny with the best egg laying pedigree possible.

The breed of hen will have a huge bearing on the number and size of eggs you will get. Bantams will obviously lay a smaller egg. They take up less space and eat a little less, but in reality the space needed for a normal size hen is not much bigger. By contrast, the difference in egg size is enormous!

Nutritional Value of an Egg

	Contents	% Daily Allowance	
Calories	70		
Fat	5g	8%	
Saturated	1.5g	8%	
Cholesterol	190mg		
Sodium	55mg	2%	
Carbohydrate	0g		
Fibre	0g		
Sugars	0g		
Protein	6g		
Vitamin A		8%	Helps maintain healthy skin and eye tissue, and assists in night vision
Vitamin B12		30%	Aids in red blood cell formation

	Contents	% Daily Allowance	
Vitamin D		2%	Helps keep bones and teeth strong
Vitamin C		0%	
Vitamin E		6%	Acts as an antioxidant that protects your cells from damaging by-products that are formed in your body and particularly protects vitamins A and C
Riboflavin		15%	Helps tissues in your body stay healthy by allowing them to 'breathe' properly
Calcium		0%	
Iron		2%	Caries oxygen to the cells and keeps blood healthy
Niacin		6%	Helps release energy and promotes normal nerve function
Folate		15%	Aids in red blood cell formation
Lutein	Trace		Are important for maintaining good vision. Can help decrease the risk of cataracts
Zeaxanthin	Trace		
Choline	Trace	50%	Has been shown to play a strong role in brain development and function One egg has half your daily requirement.
Thiamin	Trace		
Selenium	Trace		
Phosphorus	Trace		
Zinc	Trace		
Magnesium	Trace		
Iodine	Trace		
Pantothenic Acid	Trace		

Eggs are a source of high quality protein, essential for building and repairing body tissue. Muscles, organs, skin, hair as well as antibodies, enzymes and hormones are all made from protein. Protein is composed of 20 different amino acids. There are 9 essential amino acids the body cannot make, so they must come from foods. Eggs are one of the few foods considered to be a complete protein source because they provide all 9 essential amino acids as well as 9 nonessential ones. With a biological value of protein a 93.7%, eggs score higher than any other food. The egg white consists mainly of high quality protein. In fact, the protein in an egg is so ideal that it has been used as the standard against which other foods are judged. Protein is the basic material of life. We need it for building and repairing body tissues and producing antibodies, which fight infection.

Eggs are one of the few foods which naturally contain Vitamin D.

Cholesterol makes up 4% of an egg's fat profile. The fat breakdown is:

Cholesterol	4%
Lecithin	13%
Saturates	31%
Monounsaturates	38%
Poytunsaturates	14%

More than half of an egg's fat content is unsaturated and less than a third is saturated.

Collecting Eggs

The ideal is to collect fresh, clean eggs that do not need to be washed. The nest box conditions where the egg is laid will determine the cleanliness of the egg, so regular cleaning or replacement of the nest box bedding is essential. One suggestion is to use a man made material, such as the

plastic green grass used in butcher's window displays. This will need to be washed regularly, depending on how soiled it gets. The entrance to the nest boxes will need to be kept as clean as possible to prevent the hen's feet dirtying the eggs already in the nest box. Regular collection of the eggs will help and it follows that the collecting hands should also be clean. Rollaway nest boxes, where the eggs roll into a collection tray are ideal.

You will recall that the eggshell is porous. The aim is to keep the egg as clean as possible as any dirt that is not washed off quickly has a chance to penetrate the pores of the shell. For the same reason, they should be stored away from strong smells or substances.

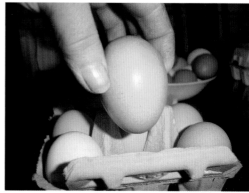
Storing eggs pointy side down

Eggs should be stored in cartons in cool, clean conditions. (10–12oc). Eggs in a carton in a fridge that does not go down below freezing is best. They are also best in the main body of the fridge, rather than in the door, where the temperature can fluctuate.

Eggs should be placed in the carton pointy side down for two reasons. Firstly, the shell is thicker and therefore stronger at the pointy end and secondly, the air sac is at the round end. If the egg is stored upside down, the air sac is trying to rise up through the egg. If the egg is almost a round shape, your best guess will do!

Storing Eggs

There are some surprising methods of long term egg storage. The only thing to remember is that if the eggs are stored as fresh eggs, they must be fully cooked on coming out of store, before being eaten.

1. A traditional method is to use waterglass, also known as sodium silicate, available to order from a chemist. Add one part waterglass to nine parts of water in a container with a close fitting lid. It was usually a ceramic bowl and lid, but now a plastic food container with a clip lid is best. Place the fresh eggs into the mixture, making sure the shells are clean and free

of any, even hairline, cracks. Eggs can be added daily until the container is full, but the water mixture must cover the eggs entirely, with nothing breaking the water mix surface. Store the container in a cool place. Eggs stored this way should keep up to 6 months.

2. The same method can be used with a lime water mix instead of waterglass. The storage time of 6 months is the same. In this case, two parts slaked lime and one part salt are added to sixteen parts of water. Lime is available from a chemist.

3. Eggs can also be individually coated as a way of preserving them. Paraffin wax or lard were traditionally used, but were replaced with gum arabic, available from chemists. Mix the gum arabic in equal measure with water and paint one side of the egg, making sure the surface is completely covered. Place the partially painted egg on a tin foil covered tray to dry. When dry, paint the remaining shell. When fully coated and dry, label and store in cartons in a cool place. Eggs stored this way should keep up to 3 months.

4. Eggs can also be pickled; a fish and chip shop favourite. Hard-boil the eggs and plunge the hard boiled eggs into cold water immediately after taking them off the heat, to prevent a green ring forming around the yolk. Then peel them ready for pickling. To prepare the pickling vinegar, use either cider or wine vinegar in a stainless steel saucepan with a pickling spice sachet. Use the amount of vinegar needed to fill the container you are using, taking into account the displacement of the eggs. Pickling spice sachets can be bought, or you can make your own with spices of your choice tied in a piece of muslin. Heat the vinegar and spice to boiling point and boil for three minutes. Then leave to cool.

Place the eggs in glass jars, remove the spice sachet and fill the jars with the cold pickling vinegar. Make sure there are no trapped air bubbles. Make sure the eggs are fully covered and put the lids on tightly. The eggs will keep for about 2 months and acquire a distinct flavour.

5. Salt can be used in a number of ways in preserving eggs. Make up a brine solution with one part salt to ten parts water and store the eggs in a

container with a tight fitting lid and the eggs fully covered. Fresh eggs in clean, crack free shells will store for about a month this way. Oven dried cooking salt can be packed around fresh eggs in a container. Fill the base with salt and layer the eggs over each other with salt in between. Eggs can keep up to 6 months this way, but it can be prone to problems if the salt is allowed to absorb water.

6. Eggs can also be frozen, but not in their shells. The various elements listed below can be kept for up to 3 months in a freezer. Thaw frozen eggs, or part eggs overnight in the fridge.

   a. Whole eggs. Beat as many eggs as you are using until just blended. Pour them into freezer containers, label with the date and number of eggs and freeze.

   b. Whites. Break and separate the eggs, being careful not to break the yolk. Pour the separated whites as they are into freezer containers and seal tightly. Mark the container with the date and number of eggs and freeze. Alternatively freeze each egg white in an ice cube tray and then transfer them to a labelled container. This makes the quantity easy to calculate on thawing.

   c. Yolks. Egg yolks need a little more care. The gelation property of yolk causes it to thicken or gel when frozen. If frozen as-is it will become so gloopy that it will be impossible to use when thawed. The trick is to beat either 1/8 teaspoon of salt or 11/2 teaspoons sugar into 4 yolks. Put into freezer container and label with number of yolks and what has been added. The salt added yolks can be used in main dishes and the sweet version in baking and deserts.

   d. Hard boiled yolks. Hard boiled yolks can be frozen to be used later for toppings or garnishes. Carefully place the separated yolks in a single layer in a saucepan and add enough boiling water to come at least 1 inch above the yolks. Cover and bring quickly to just boiling. Remove from the heat and let the saucepan stand covered for 15 mins. Remove the cooked yolks with a slotted spoon, drain well and put in a freezer container.

e. Hard boiled whole eggs or cooked whites become tough and watery when frozen, so don't freeze these.

f. How to use frozen eggs. Substitute 2 tablespoons thawed egg white for 1 large fresh egg white. Substitute 1 tablespoon thawed egg yolk for 1 fresh egg yolk. Substitute 3 tablespoons whole thawed egg for 1 large fresh egg.

7. A surprising way to use and keep eggs is to make lemon curd. See the recipe section for details. Also consider making plain sponge cakes which can be defrosted and made into an instant cake or used as sponge bases in a trifle.

How To Tell A Fresh Egg

1. Light held behind an egg will illuminate the contents, a process known as candling. The size of the air cell at the larger round end is a guide to the freshness. When the egg is newly laid, the air cell between the membrane around the albumen and the membrane on the inside of the shell is very small, about 3mm. The older the egg gets, the larger the air cell becomes. The round end of the shell has most of the pores and thus air passes through into the egg at a greater rate here. If the air sac exceeds 6mm, the egg should not be sold.

2. A fresh egg placed on a bowl of water will sink to the bottom and lie on its side. An older egg will sink and stand up on one end. If really old it will float. As the air cell increases with age, it affects the buoyancy of the egg, causing the egg to float.

3. When broken, the yolk of a fresh egg will sit up high and the white is thick and cloudy around the yolk. An older egg has a flat yolk with a thin skin and a runny, watery white.

4. The deterioration of an egg is due to an increase in the air sac and evaporation from the white and yolk. The yolk and albumen together contain about 65% water, which evaporates over time through the pores in the shell. Certain

egg shapes lose water faster than others. Storage circumstances will also affect water loss. Eggs stored in a warm dry environment will lose water, and thus age faster, than those kept in cool, humid conditions. Eggs will last longer in a fridge and if this contains a bowl of water, the egg will lose very little water, remaining fresh for longer.

5.   As water evaporates, the air sac increases in size and the egg contents decrease in volume. These changes cause the egg membranes to stretch in some places and relax in others. This means the egg contents will move around more if the egg is shaken. So shaking an egg can tell the age of it.

6.   Can you tell the difference between a fresh egg and a hard boiled egg? Spin it! A hard boiled egg spins longer because the liquid centre in a fresh egg stops it from building up enough momentum.

Eggs In General

The colour of the yolk will depend on the hen's diet. They can even be orange if there is a lot of grass meal or maize meal in the feed. Hens ranging on grass in spring and summer will lay eggs with a darker yolk than when ranging in the winter, when the grass has stopped growing. Some layers mash and pellets will contain a yolk enhancer, such as canthaxathin.

Here's one for those interested in genetics. The male chicken gets the prolific egg laying factor, amongst others, from his mother and passes it on to his daughters. Thus the sons of a hen displaying the desired quality, or, just as importantly, not displaying undesired qualities, will be used in breed selection. This is particularly important when forming hybrids. For example, Black Rocks are always a first cross hybrid, so are always produced from a Rhode Island Red cockerel and a Barred Plymouth Rock hen. The careful choice of the cockerel will ensure the high quality of the progeny and has contributed largely to the Black Rock's success.

Raw eggs. Official advice for the consumer is still to avoid eating raw eggs or foods containing raw eggs, especially for pregnant women, young children, the elderly and anyone feeling unwell.

EU Egg Weight Grades	
Very Large	73g and over
Large	63g up to 72g
Medium	53g up to 62g
Small	52g and under

If you drop an egg, an easy way to clear it up is to cover it in salt and leave it for 10 minutes. It will then clear up easily.

Eggs are one of the few foods to naturally contain Vitamin D.

Cooking With Eggs

Do not use cracked eggs under any circumstances.

Serve eggs and egg rich foods immediately after cooking, or refrigerate and use within three days.

If your eggs are in the fridge and the recipe calls for eggs at room temperature, immerse them in water for a few minutes.

The egg yolk and white separate best when they are cold.

Egg whites will beat to a better volume if they are allowed to stand at room temperature for 20 to 30 minutes before beating.

To soft boil an egg, lower the egg on a spoon into simmering water. If the water is boiling too vigorously, it will bang the egg around and break it. 4 minutes cooking will give you a runny yolk and 5–6 minutes will cook the yolk though, but still leave it soft.

When hard-boiling an egg, cook for 8 minutes in simmering, not boiling water and then cool immediately in cold water. This will stop the egg from cooking further and prevent a greenish ring forming around the yolk. If you do find such a ring, despite your precautions, there is no harm in eating it.

Cook scrambled eggs over a medium to low heat for fluffy, thick eggs. Occasionally, a large batch of scrambled egg can turn green. The colour change is harmless, but a little off-putting. It is due to a chemical change which happens when the eggs are cooked at too high a temperature or hang around for too long. Using stainless steel equipment and cooking at low temperatures will help, as will cooking in small batches and serving immediately.

Use very fresh eggs when making poached eggs.

Add water to omelettes, instead of milk. The water will turn to steam thus producing a light, airy omelette.

Use a glass or metal bowl when making meringue. The film on a plastic bowl can prevent the whites from foaming up.

Unless otherwise specified, most recipes are assuming you are using large eggs.

Egg Conversion Table

Recipe	Extra Large	Medium	Small
1 large egg	1	1	2
2 large eggs	2	2	3
3 large eggs	3	4	4
4 large eggs	3	5	6
5 large eggs	4	6	7
6 large eggs	5	7	8

Brown Egg Layer List

The first listed hens with (t) or (h) are more readily available. (t) denotes traditional and (h) denotes hybrid.

Light Brown	Brown	Darker Brown	Blueish/Green
Rhode Island Red (t)	Australorp (t)	Maran (t)	Cream Legbar (t)
Light Sussex (t)	Bowans Nera (h)	Welsummer (t)	Araucana (t)
Barnvelder (t)	Calder Ranger (h)	Speckledy (h)	Rumpless Game
Wyandotte (t)	Hisex Ranger (h)		
Plymouth Rock (t)	Black Rock (h)		
ISA Brown (h)	Hebden Black (h)		
Lohmann Brown (h)	Barnevelder		
Bovans Goldline (h)	Croad Lansghan		
Babcock Ranger (h)	Dominique		
Australorp	Hy-line Brown		
Cooted Bantam	Lohman Brown		
Brahma	Modern Langshan		
Cochin	Rhodebar		
Faverolles	Wellbar		
Fayoumi			
German Langshan			
Indian (Cornish) Game			
Jersey Giant			
New Hampshire Red			
North Holland Blue			
Orpington			
Rhode Island Red			
Wyandotte			

White Egg Layer List

White	Cream/White	White/Tinted	Cream
Andalusion	Ancona	Asil	Faverolles
Appenzeller	Breda	Derbyshire Redcap	Fayoumi
Augsburger	Japanese Bantam	Dorking	Ko-Shamo Bantam
Braabanter	Legbar	Frizzle	Nankin-Shamo Bantam
Brakel	Pekin Bantam	Ixworth	Sulmtaler

Bresse	Rosecomb Bantam	Lakenvelder	Vorwerk
Campine	Sebright Bantam	La Felche	Yamato-Gunkei
Creve Coeur		Malay	
Fresian		Marsh Dairy	
Hamburgh		Modern Game	
Doudan		Nankin Bantam	
Italiener		Norfolk Grey	
Kraienkoppe		Old English Game	
Leghorn		Old English Pheasant Fowl	
Minorca		Orloff	
Poland		Plymouth Rock	
Rhienlander		Scots Dumpy	
Sicilian Buttercup		Shamo	
Spanish		Silie	
Sultan		Sussex	
Sumatra		Tuzo Bantam	
		Wybar	
		Yokoama	
		Transylvanian Naked Neck	

Breed List

Breed	Colour of Eggs	Breed	Colour of Eggs
A			
Ancona	Cream/white	Asil	White/Tinted
Andalusian	White	Augsburger	White
Appenzeller	White	Australorp	Tinted/Brown
Araucana	Blue-Green		
B			
Barnevelder	Brown	Black Rock	Brown
Bovans Nera	Brown	Brakel	White
Braabanter	White	Breda	Cream/White
Brahma	Tinted/Brown	Bresse	White

C

Calder Ranger	Mid Brown	Cream Legbar	Blue-Green/Olive
Campine	White	Creve Coeur	White
Cochin	Tinted/Brown	Croad Langghan	Brown
Cooted Bantam	Tinted		

D

Derbyshire Redcap	White/Tinted	Doudan	White
Dominque	Brown	Dutch Bantum	Tinted
Dorking	White/Tinted		

F

Faverolles	Tinted Cream	Fresian	White
Fayoumi	Tinted Cream	Frizzle	White tinted

G

German Langshan	Tinted Brown		

H

Hamburgh	White	Hisex Ranger	Brown
Hebden Black	Mid to dark brown	Hy-Line Brown	Brown

I

Indian (Cornish) Game	Tinted/Brown	Italiener	White
ISA Brown	Brown	Ixworth	White/Tinted

J

Japanese Bantum	Cream/White	Jersey Giant	Tinted Brown

K

Ko-Shamo Bantum	Tinted Cream	Kraienkoppe	White

L

Lakenvelder	Tinted white	La Fleche	Tinted White
Legbar	White/cream	Lohmann Brown	Brown
Leghorn	White		

M

Malay	Tinted	Modern Game	Tinted
Maran	Dark Brown speckled	Minorca	White
Marsh Daisy	Tinted	Modern Langshan	Brown

N

Breed	Colour	Breed	Colour
Nankin Bantum	Tinted	Norfolk Grey	Tinted
Nankin-Shamo Bantum	Tinted cream	North Holland Blue	Tinted Brown
New Hampshire Red	Tinted Brown		

O

Breed	Colour	Breed	Colour
Old English Game	Tinted	Orloff	Tinted
Old English Pheasant Fowl	Tinted White	Orpington	Brown Tinted

P

Breed	Colour	Breed	Colour
Pekin Bantam	Cream White	Poland	White
Plymouth Rock	Tinted		

R

Breed	Colour	Breed	Colour
Rhienlander	White	Rosecomb Bantam	White/Cream
Rhode Island Red	Tinted Brown	Rumpless Game	Blue-green
Rhodebar	Brown		

S

Breed	Colour	Breed	Colour
Scots Dumpy	Tinted	Spanish	White
Scots Grey	White Tinted	Speckeldy	Dark Brown Speckled
Sebright Bantam	CreamWhite	Sulmtaler	Cream/Tinted
Shamo	Tinted/White	Sultan	White
Sicilian Buttercup	White	Sumatra	White
Silie	White/Tinted	Sussex	Tinted

T

Breed	Colour	Breed	Colour
Tuzo Bantam	Tinted	Transylvanian Naked Neck	Tinted/White

V

Breed	Colour	Breed	Colour
Vorwerk	Cream/Tinted		

W

Breed	Colour	Breed	Colour
Welbar	Brown	Wyandotte	Tinted/Brown
Welsummer	Dark Brown, speckled	Wybar	Tinted
White Star	White		

Y

Breed	Colour	Breed	Colour
Yamato-Gunkei	Tinted/Cream	Yokohama	Tinted/White

11

Selling Eggs

This chapter sets out the rules and regulations on selling eggs. It is not all as simple as you may think, so beware the pitfalls.

Egg Quality

Eggs to be sold should have no shell faults such as cracks, even hairline cracks or any other type of damage. They should not be dirty, but equally they should not be washed. The aim is to produce clean eggs that do not need washing and this is covered in the Housing chapter. Washed eggs can, however, be sold at the farm gate, your own stall, or personally door to door, because the producer can be asked personally about the origin of the eggs. Basically the only eggs that cannot be sold in person are ones which are damaged in any way. It is not possible to sell any eggs, under any circumstances, which have been laid when the hens have a cockerel in their midst.

Egg quality is classified as either A, B or C. The lower grades of B and C include dirty, damaged or washed eggs, which are sent for industrial use if bought by a packer. A packer is described a bit later. Eggs sold either as a surplus or as a small business should aim to meet the requirements of an A designation. These are:

a. A cuticle (outer layer or bloom) that is normal, clean and undamaged. Washing will damage the cuticle.

b. No wet or dry cleaning

c. A shell which is normal, clean and undamaged. This would exclude any misshapen or cracked eggs.

d. An air cell that does not exceed 6mm in height.

e. Albumen that is clear and has a gelatinous consistency. The albumen should be free of any foreign bodies.

f. A yolk that is free of foreign bodies and which does not move appreciably on rotation of the egg.

g. No foreign smell.

Rules for marketing eggs started in June 2004, when a requirement was introduced for producers to stamp eggs when they were being sold as graded eggs. The stamping codes are explained further down.

From 1 July 2005, ungraded eggs, as well as graded eggs, need to be stamped where they are sold at local public markets, whether sold by you, or a stall you have given or sold the eggs to. Furthermore, if eggs are sold at public markets, the premises on which the eggs are laid will need to be registered with the Egg Marketing Inspectorate of DEFRA, irrespective of how many hens you keep. So, selling eggs at a local public market such as street markets and Farmer's Markets is subject to strict regulation.

However, before your heart sinks even further, the Regulations say that you do not need to register your flock or stamp your eggs if:

a. You have less than 350 hens and

b. You sell the eggs ungraded and

c. You sell at the farm gate or personally door to door.

I have assumed that this book is aimed at people who can tick all three of the above and are therefore not covered by the Regulations. However, for the sake of completeness, as you never know, your flock may be more than 350 one day, I will continue with the Regulations.

You must register the premises if you have 350 hens or more wherever you are selling the eggs, but you do not need to stamp the eggs if you are selling them ungraded and selling at the farm gate or personally door to door. If the eggs are sold at public market they will need to be stamped.

However, you do need to register and stamp your eggs if you are selling the eggs at a local market or to a packing station. This applies no matter how many hens you have.

The idea of stamping eggs is for traceability. The stamp code is unique for each producer and is a number/letters/number format. The first number denotes the type of production:

0 - organic

1 - free range

2 - barn

3 - cage

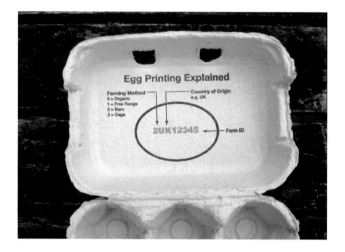

Next the letters denote the county of origin and finally the last numbers are the registered flock number. Next time you see eggs sold at a Farmer's Market have a look (because I am assuming you are no longer going to buy supermarket eggs!).

So even if you are selling the eggs yourself at a local Women's Institute or Farmer's market they have to be stamped. This is to prove that you are the person who has produced them. In the past, eggs could have come from anywhere and been sold at these markets, so the regulations have tightened the traceability and origins of the eggs sold at market. The regulations even extend to a gift for a local raffle prize, where the eggs should be stamped. If given to a charity shop or auctions for a charity they have to be graded & stamped as they are given to an unknown third party.

As soon as you sell eggs to a third party other than a market stall, such as a local shop or butcher, you must register as a packer. A packer has to register as such with the Egg Marketing Inspectorate of DEFRA and meet certain criteria with regard to egg quality, weight, storage, stamping, packaging and presentation for sale. There is no minimum output of eggs needed to register as a packer.

Alternatively you can sell all your eggs to a packer. The advantage is that the packer will take all your eggs, even the small or damaged ones (these will go for industrial use). The disadvantages are that you have no control of price and you need to be able to provide a continuous supply of eggs all year round, regardless of the moult and seasonal light.

Egg boxes will be needed at whatever level you are selling eggs, with the exception of selling them to a packer. Most people are willing to keep their egg boxes for you to give you a start, but once they are customers they will hopefully only be using your boxes! That brings two pressures on your egg box stock in that they will no longer be introducing new boxes to the stock and you have to ensure that they bring their egg boxes back. I used to write a message on mine asking for the box back and for any others they may come across and now I have a sticky label saying the same thing, but my box stock still goes down. I had hoped that once I had printed 40 labels that would be it, but I print a new sheet of labels once a fortnight. I have asked the parents at my daughter's primary school to bring boxes in for me and without that I would have difficulties. The alternative is to buy boxes, but that is an additional cost to take into account. The one enquiry I made had a minimum order of 500 boxes.

So start planning your egg box source long before you need them. Also consider putting a message on them telling the recipient about your hens and asking for the box back.

How much do you charge? I think my eggs compare with the best that Marks & Spencer sell. However farm eggs can be bought in a number of butcher shops for half the price. You can work out the cost of food for a week, or work out how long a bag of food lasts. Use a week's egg production against the cost of food for a week or the egg production for the length of time a bag lasts and that will give you the basic cost of the eggs. Add to that an amount for the grit, oyster shell, poultry spice etc and that will give a truer cost. The other way to look at is that you have to feed the hens anyway and you are only selling surplus eggs, in which case they are free of cost!

Photo by Stéphane Rocher

12

Incubation

Incubation is the next step after keeping chickens for a while. There is an irresistible appeal in watching your future hens hatch and grow up with you. Whether you hire an incubator or intend to buy one, read this chapter first to avoid any costly mistakes.

Planning

The move into hatching your own eggs will need some planning beforehand. If you plan to buy fertile eggs in, then the planning will start with the careful choice of incubator and even more careful selection of fertile egg supplier.

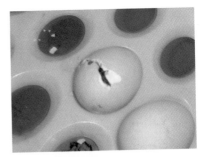

If you plan to hatch eggs from your own chickens then the planning will need to start a lot earlier. The age, health and quality of your breeding stock will determine the quality of your chicks. It goes without saying that the successful continuation of any breed will depend entirely on the quality of each generation. Only use the best quality breeding stock in tip top condition and in the prime of their breeding calendar. Replace their layers pellets with breeder pellets to give the birds all the nutrition they need to produce healthy chicks. Lack of essential vitamins and minerals can lead to a number of chick deformities, often blamed on the incubator, but actually due to an inadequate diet for the parents. See the Problem Solving section for effects of dietary deficiency.

In the wild, nature will select the desired breeding stock by survival of the fittest. You have stepped into the shoes of Mother Nature and need to take your responsibility seriously. What are the chicks required to achieve? Is it just the fun of raising a few

chicks for the fun and education of doing so, or is there a breed survival programme in place? Even more radical is the design of a new hybrid bred specifically for one, or a number of, desired traits. This has happened recently with the introduction of a new hybrid producing very dark brown eggs and one producing blue eggs.

It is often said in cattle that the bull is half the herd. The same applies to the chosen cockerel and he must display the absolute best qualities. If you are buying a cockerel buy the best one you can. A second year cockerel would be best as he will come with a track record of his first year. He will be more fertile later in the year than a first year cockerel, which leads to the saying 'wait until the cock has had the sun on his back'. If the hens have had another cockerel in the pen who was being housed with them, but with no intention of incubating the eggs, there has to be a run off of at least 3 weeks before putting her in with the desired cockerel for breeding. Sperm can live in the hen's oviduct for up to 3 weeks and a time lapse is therefore essential.

Remember that there will be about a 50/50 split between hen and cockerel chicks. This is an average and some batches may be predominantly cockerels. What are you going to do with them? Are you prepared to cull them yourself?

The chicks will not have the benefit of vaccination that is received by the point of lay chickens from a reputable supplier because of the lack of single batch vaccinations, so disease control will be totally reliant on good cleanliness and biosecurity.

If the resultant fertile eggs and/or chicks are to be sold, the parent stock should be tested for inherited diseases. These are detected by blood test undertaken by a vet. This is important because a number of diseases may not manifest themselves in the parents, but may have disastrous consequences for the chicks.

The Broody

At this point forget everything horrible I have written about bantams because their tendency to go broody will be a wonderful asset if you want to raise your own chicks. A good, reliable broody is worth her weight in gold as she will save you a lot of time, effort and expense. Not only will she hatch the chicks, she will teach them the necessary life skills and defend them with her life if necessary. It is a wonderful sight to see a broody hen call and watch the chicks run to shelter under her outstretched, loving wings.

A broody will benefit from bespoke accommodation and a little extra care. Obviously, she can simply take up one of the nest boxes in the hen house, but she and the other residents will benefit from a separate broody coop. This will keep

her in comfort and allow the hen house nest boxes to be used as usual. A broody coop will have a flat, solid floor, solid sides and back and be the size to accommodate a hen comfortably with space to stretch her legs and house a food station.

The roof should slope from front to back and be removable, or have a hinged opening. It is much easier to lift hens, egg, and chicks out of the top than the front. The front of a broody coop is the biggest distinguishing factor. It is an open construction, made of slats placed so that the chicks can move in and out between them, but not the hen. This will allow you to feed the chicks on chick crumbs, which the hen would eat before the chicks had even found the bowl, if she was given the chance. One slat, usually the middle one is made so that it can slide up or out altogether, to let the hen out when you want to. The usual criteria of being watertight and draught proof still apply. Because of the open slatted front, careful thought should be given to the siting of the coop.

Inside the coop should be a nest area and an area for food and water. Do not lift her off her nest, or otherwise encourage her to eat and drink. She will do so in her own time and usually when you are not looking. A tip for the nest area is to use a section of turf. This will provide some dampness and prevent the eggs drying out.

Having provided a practical and comfortable broody area all that is needed is a broody hen and some fertile eggs. Tell tale broody signs are a savage peck when you lift her to collect the eggs and a hissing, growling noise warning you off. Give her a dusting of mite powder before you put her into the broody coop, paying extra attention under her wings. Mite will be most uncomfortable for her and if she wriggles too much she could damage the eggs. There is also the danger of passing them on to the vulnerable chicks, so prevention is always best. Give her some infertile eggs or dummy eggs to begin with and leave her for 24 hours. If she has settled down on the eggs when you next check on her the signs are good and fertile eggs can be introduced under her. If, however, she leaves the nest and makes a break for freedom when you lift the lid, it is time to send her back to the main flock. There is always a danger that this will happen, which is why it is wise to be sure she is broody before putting the fertile eggs under her. Fertile eggs can be held for a while at room temperature, providing they are turned regularly, but once they are warmed up and incubation has started, a drop in temperature if the hen leaves and there is no immediate replacement, will terminate the embryo growth and ruin the eggs.

If A Broody Is Not To Hand

Equipment needed for successful incubation without a broody

+ Incubator

+ Incubator thermometer

+ Humidity meter

+ Egg candler

+ Brooder unit

+ Chick crumb feeder

+ Chick crumbs

+ Narrow lipped drinker

Incubators

My advice on the purchase of an incubator is to get the absolute best you can afford. There are many incubators on the market and it is best to do a little research before deciding on the one for you. If possible, see if you can borrow one first to get and idea of the amount of commitment the different types require. As well as choosing an incubator, check on the support available and the after-sales service as I have discovered these to be invaluable.

There are three types of incubator; manual, semi-automatic and automatic. The manual ones are a heated compartment where the eggs will need to be turned individually. My advice is to avoid this kind as they really are hard work. The semi-automatic ones have a system where all the eggs are turned at once, but by a mechanism where the owner operates the turning device. This is obviously less time consuming than turning each egg individually, but you still have to be available 5 times a day to operate the lever. The automatic incubators are the ultimate and definitely to be recommended. There is a choice in the manual and semi-automatic incubators between a fan or no fan. It will always be better to go for one with a fan. Even with a fan there can still be cold spots, but these are significantly less likely.

Having decided on the type of incubator, the next decision is the egg capacity required. Most fertile eggs are sold in multiples of 6 and if you are collecting your eggs from your own breeding stock you will need to batch them if you are only using one incubator. If you are using two, then in theory you can treat each egg as an individual and move it from the first incubator to the hatching incubator on 19 days.

Treat your first few batches as a steep learning curve and treat any that hatch as a huge achievement. There are so many variables and each incubator is individual that you need to get to know it and how best to operate it. Keep as detailed records as you can as these will be invaluable in diagnosing what went wrong and even what you did right!

As you move forward and get bitten by the incubation bug, you may benefit from a separate incubator to use solely for hatching. This keeps the incubation incubator free of contamination and allows the next batch of eggs to be started almost before the current batch has hatched. I have ended up in this position by accident in that the first incubator I bought is a manual egg turning one and I do not have the time to attend to it 5 times a day. It is, however, perfect for hatching, so I move the eggs into there just before they are about to pip.

There are 5 features to take into account when choosing an incubator.

- ◆ Egg turning
- ◆ Temperature control
- ◆ Humidity control
- ◆ Fan assisted
- ◆ After sales support

Egg Turning

I would suggest that the ones to avoid are incubators which have no egg turning facility at all. These will be completely manual and involve turning each egg individually. A good start may be with one where the eggs are turned manually, but with ease. This involves a sliding floor which is pushed or pulled with the use of a handle. Pulling the floor will turn the eggs one way and pushing the handle will return the floor to the staring position and turn the eggs back again.

It is vital, however the eggs are turned, to turn them one way and then back again. Do not keep turning them in the same direction. This is because the yolk is suspended in the centre of the egg, much like a hammock, by two chords, called chalazae. If the egg is continually turned the same way, the chalazae will be wound tighter and tighter and a developing chick would not survive.

It is also important to turn them an uneven number of times a day. This makes sure that the egg lies on alternate sides over night. A minimum of three turns a day is necessary, with five times a day being better. Regular turning ensures that the embryo does not become stuck to one part of the shell.

Egg turning alone may be the biggest influence in your choice of incubator. My first one was one with a moving floor operated by handle and I found being available to turn the eggs three times on a week day and five times on weekend days, for a continuous 19 days was a real struggle. I managed it, just, and immediately resolved to buy an automatic incubator. My new one automatically turns the eggs every hour and even plays a little tune while it does it!

Temperature control

A basic incubator will give little or no temperature adjustment facility. My first one didn't and I managed to hatch eggs with it. The lack of temperature control, however, is not ideal as a developing egg needs a constant temperature of 37.8ºC for the first 18 to 19 days during the incubation stage and a lesser temperature of 37.4ºC for the last 2 to 3 days, known as the hatching stage. The two temperatures are not hugely different, but the aim is to provide optimum conditions to produce a live, healthy chick. The success rate will be better in an incubator with temperature control. An essential in the incubator is a fan. This will ensure even temperature control in all areas and avoid cold patches.

An incubator thermometer will be very useful in monitoring the temperature if the machine does not do it electronically itself. Get into the habit of recording the temperature at least daily and each time you turn the eggs, if that is what you are doing.

Humidity control

Much the same as temperature, the humidity requirements are different for the incubation and hatching stages. A humidity of 35% is needed for incubation and rises to 70% for hatching. At the pipping stage where the chick makes the first crack and then a small hole in the shell it is easier for the chick if the membranes in the egg are not too moist. The next stage, of splitting the shell open and getting out is easier if the membranes are moist. If they are too dry the chick will become stuck to them and will die, effectively imprisoned in the shell.

Most incubators now will need you to fill a compartment with water and in the case of an electronic incubator filling the water trough as and when required is the only active participation you will have for the 21 days the eggs are in it. You will need to judge the humidity level for yourself in a manual incubator and a humidity meter will help you with this. When putting water into the incubator it is the surface area of the water that is important, not the actual volume of water.

More chicks are lost to the humidity being too high, rather than too low. If the humidity is high, the chick swells up because it absorbs too much water and then can't move around in the shell to chip its way out. I have a humidity controller on my big incubator and that has not drawn up any water to put into the machine for months. The hatch rate has risen as a result of getting the humidity meter and makes the subject of humidity even more mystifying. It really is a case of keeping records and getting to know your incubator.

Fan Assisted

Fan assistance in an incubator works much the same way as in a fan assisted oven. The fan serves to evenly distribute the warmth and humidity around the incubator, giving each egg an equal chance. This is obviously a desirable feature and most incubators sold have it.

After Sales

In the case of incubation, the after sales service should include help in analysing what went wrong with the hatch as well as the usual service of dealing with any machine failure. There are so many pitfalls for the beginner that it is important when buying your machine

Where To Put The Incubator

The siting of the incubator needs thoughtful care. It should be in an area at constant room temperature without fluctuations and preferably not centrally heated, as that can be a dry atmosphere. It needs to be placed so that it is free from any danger of being knocked or disturbed and is best in a room which is not in constant use. It should be placed out of direct sunlight because of the heating factor and, I feel, is better in darkness. I put a cover over mine. This is because if the eggs were under a broody they would be in darkness most of the time.

Your incubator should be plugged into its own dedicated plug socket and not one it will have to share with the vacuum cleaner, for example. It will also be useful to have another free socket nearby so that you can plug the egg candler in without having to travel with an egg to another location or be tempted, heaven forbid, to disconnect the incubator temporarily.

Power cuts cannot be helped. If one is only for a short duration there may be no harm done as eggs under a broody will be left for short periods. A fertile egg will hold its temperature longer than a non fertile one, which is how a broody will know which ones to eject from the nest. If she comes back to a cold egg, out it goes. A longer power cut will unfortunately result in the loss of the chicks, but a blanket wrapped around the incubator will keep it warm longer and may save the day.

Eggs To Be Incubated

Eggs to be incubated should be smooth and uniform, not rough or misshapen. They should be a medium size. Small eggs will hatch small chicks, which is not desirable for a good start in life. Avoid over large eggs as these may be double yolked. Eggs with shells which look like a sieve when candled, sometimes described as freckled, will generally not be fertile. Eggs to be incubated must be clean, having been laid and collected in the most hygienic conditions.

They should be set in the incubator as soon as possible after being laid. If there is a delay in going into the incubator eggs should be stored in a cool room, pointy side down in an egg box. They should be turned twice daily either by turning the box over one way and then back the other, or tilting one side and then the other if they are stored on an egg tray. Use a wedge to put under one side and then the other to achieve a tilt of the tray. I keep mine in egg boxes and turn them over always keeping the hinge of the box on the table. That way I know they have been turned alternately as sometimes it can be difficult to remember which way they were turned previously. Using the hinge as the turning point saves having to remember!

I have also had the bright idea of storing eggs to be incubated in the bottom of a rocking incubator with just the rocking motor on. This way they are automatically kept moving and no having to remember which way to turn the egg box.

Sending Fertile Eggs Through The Post

If you intend to send eggs through the post they should first be individually wrapped in a piece of kitchen towel and then put into the appropriate size polystyrene box. The two halves of the box should be firmly taped together and then the whole package should be wrapped in strong brown paper. The parcel should be clearly marked as having fragile contents and mark which way up the parcel should be kept. This will be the position in which the eggs will be held pointy side down. It can only be hoped that the parcel will be placed the right side up at each stage of its journey, but if the correct position is not clearly marked then it will be left to pure chance.

Encourage the purchaser to pay for the fastest method of postage as time is of the essence. A percentage of fertility is lost with every day that passes.

Receiving Fertile Eggs Through The Post

Check with the seller that the eggs are going to be packed and sent in accordance with the above paragraph. Be prepared to pay for the fastest method of postage for the reason explained above. Upon receipt of the eggs store them pointy side down for 24 hours before putting them in the incubator. This allows the contents to settle down after their journey. Although it delays the start of incubation safe storage for 24 hours will increase the chance of successful incubation.

Setting The Eggs

You have your incubator in a suitable location and you have your fertile eggs. In 21 days time you hope to have as many chicks as possible. There are a few precautions to take before putting the process in motion.

The incubator and eggs must be as disease free as possible. The incubator must be thoroughly cleaned and disinfected with specialist incubator disinfectant before use. The eggs must also be clean and will benefit from a wipe over with the same disinfectant.

Unless your incubator is an automatic digital one it is best to let the incubator run for a day or two before putting the eggs in. This allows for any operating problems to be sorted out before the eggs are put in. In the same way it is best to check that a suspected broody hen really is broody as discussed above, a faulty incubator will also ruin the eggs if it heats them up and then develops a problem. However, a digital incubator assumes you have put the eggs in before pressing the start button and then counts the days down, adjusting for the different phases as it goes. There is therefore no facility for starting and stopping.

Once the eggs are set and the incubation has started, resist the temptation to lift the top, or cover, off. This loses valuable heat and humidity. You will have to do so in order to candle the eggs, but that is the only time, and when doing so, just lift the lid sufficiently to get your hand in and out: don't take the whole cover off. Even more importantly, do not lift the lid once pipping has started and not until the last chick is dry. I made the easy mistake of lifting the lid on my first batch to inspect the first two hatched chicks and lost the other four as dead in shell. By letting all the humidity out at a crucial time, the membranes in the remaining eggs had become drier and trapped the chicks inside.

As soon as the eggs are in the incubator the countdown starts to the chicks hatching in 21 days time, so give some thought to the best time for you to expect the chicks. It would probably be at the weekend, in which case set the eggs on a Saturday to get chicks on a Saturday. They will be ready to move to the brooder on Sunday and you will have the time to set up the brooder and be ready for them. My daughter's class at school has had some eggs to hatch and we set them on a Wednesday. This fitted in with the school week as the chicks can be heard cheeping in their shells a day or two before they hatch. So the school week for hatching was:

Monday   chicks heard cheeping

Tuesday   pipping starts

Wednesday   chicks hatch

Thursday   chicks dry off and fluff up

Friday   chicks come home to the brooder

Egg Candling

The experts and books say that eggs should be candled at least three times, at 7 days, 14 days and 19 days. Infertile eggs should be removed as soon as they are discovered. A basic egg candler is rather like a torch with a soft rubber ring around the light source. The round end of the egg is placed into the rubber ring and the candler is switched on to illuminate the contents. To get the best view inside the egg this need to be done in as dark an environment as possible. The light should only be shone into the egg for a few seconds, just long enough to make a rapid assessment. Longer exposure to intense light may damage the chick.

Candling will show the development of the chick inside and the increasing size if the air sac at the blunt end of the egg. The size of the air sac gives two pieces of connected information on the development of the chick. If the length of incubation is in doubt, usually under a broody, rather than in an incubator, then it can be established from the size of the air sac. If the length of incubation is known, then the size of the air sac will indicate whether development of the embryo is at the correct stage. Any problems being caused by the wrong temperature or humidity can be corrected.

The first candling at 7 days will show a red spider like substance in yellowish liquid. It has a red 'body' about the size of a pea and long thin red tentacles spreading out from it. This is a wonderful sight as it means the egg is fertile and developing. There will be a small air sac at the blunt end of the shell.

Candling at 14 days will confirm that the chick is alive and growing. It will be a dark mass and the air sac is bigger.

The final candling at 19 days will find a fully grown hick who will probably move away from the light source. The air sac will seem to take up about a quarter of the shell.

Remember each time that you candle an egg the light should only be shone through for a few seconds.

Hatching

A day or so before the chicks are due to be hatched you may hear chirping coming from the eggs. This is the chick starting to communicate with its mother who would normally chirp back in encouragement. If you feel inclined, feel free to make chirping noises back and listen to the chicks as they respond.

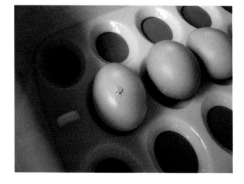

The day before hatching, so on day 20, the chick will make a first

break in the shell. A small piece of shell is chipped out and lifted off about a third of the way down the egg from the point. This is known as pipping. Nothing much will happen for a while, maybe not until the next day, but the chick's beak may be seen as it pokes out from the tiny hole every so often.

On day 21 the chick will summon up all its strength and chip the top off the pointy end, in about the same place as you would chop the top off a boiled egg. It takes its first gulp of air as it throws its head back and pushes the top off. It will have a rest after this effort, but will eventually prize the bottom half of the shell off its body. The whole process takes time and is visibly exhausting for the chick. It will pause for frequent rests for a long time after it has hatched and starts to dry. The chick should emerge wet, but with the yolk fully absorbed into its stomach. If there is any not absorbed and still outside the chick as a hernia, it will not survive.

The newly hatched chick will stagger unevenly around the incubator in between resting. Most times it seems to be giving up the ghost and about to die, only to spring back to life at the slightest stimulation. As its siblings emerge they will stumble over each other and the remaining eggs in a state of chaos. As they dry out and begin to look better they will start sparring with each other, at which point you know that all is well!

There are some which may hatch late, so do not turn the incubator off and throw any unhatched eggs away until you are sure they are not going to hatch. If you have candled them up to Day 19 you will be sure that the eggs are fertile, so give them a little extra time and they may surprise you.

Helping The Chick To Hatch

If pipping has started and there is no further progress after 24 hours although the chick is making the effort, I think it is worth trying to help the chick. There are those who say that Nature should run its course and if the chick is too weak to get out of the shell it is not a chick that will survive. I think that there is nothing to lose and that the chick's difficulty may be as a result of the humidity not being right in the incubator, not an act of Nature. Helping the chick must be done very slowly and with the utmost care. Break small pieces of shell off at a time and if there is any sign of blood stop on that part immediately.

Under no circumstances help a chick out earlier then 24 hours after day 21 as it will not be ready and will not have absorbed the last of the yolk. It will be sure to die.

Record Keeping

There are two aspects of record keeping. One is the breeding programme, how many eggs were fertile, how many hatched and quality of chicks. Records will be kept for both the hens and the cockerel. Coding the eggs with a pencil mark will enable you to identify the parents of each chick for record keeping purposes. The records are essential in deciding on the best parents to use in future.

The other aspect of record keeping is for the incubator. Location, ambient conditions such as the temperature and humidity in the room, weather conditions, season, daily record of egg turning times, when water was added, internal temperature and humidity in the incubator, the list is endless! In the beginning record keeping is essential in a 'get to know you' exercise with your new incubator. Each one is different and you will learn from your successes and failures. Record keeping will help you in your analysis as, for example, some problems can be caused by the temperature being too high or too low. If you have not kept a record of the internal temperature day by day you will not know which problem it was.

Problem Solving And Likely Causes

Brain disorders

Caused by lack of Vitamin E in the parent's diet. Chicks just stand around star gazing. Affected chicks should be culled.

Chick stuck after pipping

This is caused by insufficient humidity. Resist the urge to keep lifting the lid to check on hatching as the humid air will be released each time. Wipe the egg with a clean damp cloth to increase the humidity. The same applies under a broody. If the eggs are wiped the day before they are due to pip they will benefit from the extra humidity.

If all else fails and the chick is clearly going to die if left stuck in the shell, then there is nothing to lose in helping it out. This must be done very carefully. Break the shell off bit by bit and stop immediately if any blood is seen. Start again in another place.

Curly toes

- Caused by a lack of Vitamin B2 in the parent's diet.

Dead in shell, partly formed

Embryo stuck to one side of the shell. Egg not turned sufficiently. Ensure that the eggs are properly positioned in the incubator and that they are turned at least 5 times a day.

Death could have been caused by the temperature being either higher or lower than the desired 37.5oC during incubation.-Viral infection. Ensure parents are disease free, use strict hygiene regime for the eggs and incubator.

Can be an inherited problem. If it happens regularly change your breeding stock.

Dead in shell, fully formed

Lack of calcium and phosphorus, provided from the diet of the parents, will lead to deformed limbs and /or beak in the chick and lead to the inability for the chick to force its way out of the shell.

Humidity in the hatching stage can cause the chick to become stuck to the membrane and unable to get out of the shell. This is usually a result of the humidity being too high. The chick absorbs too much moisture and cannot turn around in the shell to unzip its way out.

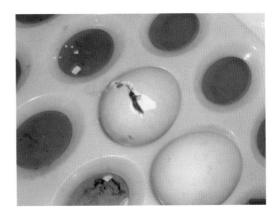

Infertile eggs

If the eggs have come from a source other than your own breeding stock, you may have been the victim of an unscrupulous seller. Fertile egg sales should be sold with the guarantee of replacement if they are found to be infertile. The cost of postage/ delivery of the replacements would be reasonable. It is worth remembering if you are looking on eBay that feedback left by other buyers of fertile eggs relates to the security of packaging and swiftness of post, not to fertility of eggs.

If the eggs are from your own stock and your cockerel is as yet unproven, he may be infertile. He may also be too old and past his prime.

Your cockerel should be properly nourished, with breeders rations preferably, and not over or under fed. An undernourished or over fat cockerel will not perform properly.

Is your cockerel with the right number of hens? If he is spread too thinly over a number of hens he will become stressed and unable to perform. A maximum of 5 hens is best.

How long were the eggs stored before being put into the incubator? Ideally they should be kept for no longer than 7 days. They should be kept at 12-15oC in humid conditions. The longer they are kept the lower the chance of remaining fertile. They also need to be kept moving while they are waiting to go into the incubator. If you keep them in an egg box turn the box over regularly, but be sure to always turn it one way, then the other. Do not keep turning the box the same way as this will wind the chalazae on either side of the yolk in much the same way that winding a hammock around would. See the chapter on eggs (How an egg is formed) for a description of the chalazae.

I store my eggs in the bottom half of an octagon incubator with the motor running. Thus they are in constant movement.

Low hatching rate

Can be as a result of a lack of Vitamin B12 in the parent's diet. A lack will mean inadequate blood formation in the chick. It could also be a lack of minerals, essential for proper development.

Hatched early

Temperature in the incubator is too high. The temperature should be reduced for pipping and hatching.

Hatched Late

Temperature in the incubator is too low. Maintain the optimum temperature of 37.5°C.

Cold areas in the incubator. Fan assisted incubators will alleviate this problem. When checking the temperature in the incubator move the thermometer around to ensure all areas are monitored.

Rickets

Caused by lack of Vitamin D in the parent's diet. The chicks look like their legs are made of rubber and can only stand with difficulty. The breast bone is often twisted. There is no cure for this. Affected chicks should be culled.

Rotten eggs

This will be caused by a bacterial infection. Damage to the egg or incorrect hygiene in the incubator can allow Escherichia coli to enter the shell and cause the contents to rot. It is usually accompanied by the recognisable rotten egg smell.

Small chicks

You incubated small eggs. They need to be at least a medium size.

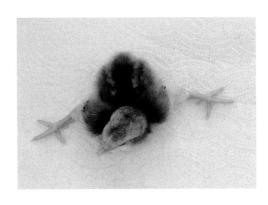

Splayed legs

This can be caused by a genetic deficiency in the parent stock and will require investigation if it is a frequent occurrence. It can also be caused by a slippery floor in the incubator or brooder. Provide the chicks with a nonslip surface with the right tray inserts in the incubator and suitable flooring in the brooder. Plain newspaper is too slippery; they need a good layer of wood shavings.

Rearing And Brooding

Once hatched, a chick has no need of food or water for 24/48 hours. The last thing it does before hatching is to absorb the yolk, giving it enough nutrition to be entirely self-sufficient for up to two days. It is for this reason that many commercial chicks are transported as day olds, allowing continuous journeys, where older chicks will require breaks for food and water. If you are lucky enough to see a wet chick emerge from the egg you will notice that it has an extended, round belly where the yolk has been absorbed in its entirety.

The newly hatched chick has no immediate need for food or water, but it does need a warm, moist environment in which to dry out and fluff up. Care also has to be taken for its siblings still preparing for the task of chipping out. They also need a warm moist environment to allow them to get out of the shell. If the surrounding air dries out, the inner membrane dries out and becomes a strong tough barrier, making it almost impossible for the chick to break out. If you notice chicks hatching with bits of dry shell stuck to them, raise the moisture level immediately. Continuously lifting the incubator lid to see how they are getting on will allow the moist air to escape and result in the later hatching chicks becoming imprisoned in the shells. Dead in shell chicks will result. There are many reasons for dead in shell chicks, but this is one that is completely avoidable. You will have raised the moisture level in the incubator in the last three days when the eggs stopped turning and it is essential to maintain the high moisture level for the entire period of hatching.

When they first hatch they can lie immobile for long periods as they recover from the exertions of hatching. Wait until they are all fully mobile, dry and fluffed up before moving them to the brooder.

The next stage in their development is just as hazardous as incubation was. The little chicks are vulnerable to changes in temperature and infection and need to be kept in a protected environment. In the same way that the incubator has to be kept clean and disinfected, so the brooder environment and equipment needs to be clean and disinfected before welcoming the chicks to their new home.

A brooder can come in any number of shapes and sizes, but the common factor is provision of a heat source, with food and water easily found nearby. Whatever the source of the heat, the chicks should be able to move away from it if they want to. An 'electric hen' type pad gives the chicks warmth and shelter underneath it. A protected heat lamp provides heat, but no shelter. The chicks need to be in an area large enough to house the

heat source and keep the food and water in an area away form it. Chicks like warm water no more than you do.

They also need to be in an environment where they can distinguish night from day. A heat lamp in a permanently lit room, for example, will not allow them the night time rest and sleep that they need. A heated pad or ceramic bulb, both of which give off heat, but not light are best. Natural daylight in their surrounding environment will give them the best start.

Having decided on the type of heat source, attention needs to be turned to the container. It will need to have enough floor space for the chicks to get away from the heat if they need to, as well as space to house the feeder and drinker. The floor surface is the next consideration. A flat, slippery surface is to be avoided at all cost. The chicks will slip and slide about and will be prone to 'splayed legs'. One this happens it is very difficult to get their legs back into position and will result in the chick being culled out of kindness. Wood shavings on the floor will help, as will rubber matting, such as car mats for example. Most commercial brooders use a mesh floor, either plastic or metal and I have certainly found that this works best. Consider also the floor in the incubator used for hatching as this also must not be slippery. A newly hatched chick needs as safe an environment as possible.

Next, consider the sides of the brooder. At first the chicks will stay on the ground, but they will be growing feathers from day one and will soon be able to jump and flutter. An open box, or cardboard surround will work for the first week, but a lid of some sort will soon need to be found. The metal cages sold for dogs are ideal. Finally, find a good place to put the brooder. The downstairs toilet seems a popular option! It needs to be in a draught proof location, with a fairly constant temperature and access to light, preferably daylight. I keep mine in the summer house, which works well.

When the chicks are ready to be transferred to the brooder make sure it is ready for them in advance. The brooder unit needs to be warm and ready before the chicks are transferred. The incubator will be at 37.4°C and the brooder unit needs to be a similar temperature to ensure a smooth transition for the chicks. Use a thermometer and use the dimmer switch, or adjust the height of the lamp to achieve the desired temperature. Heat lamps do not need start up time, but the heat pads do. Put the water and chick trough full of chick crumbs in the brooder and you are ready to introduce the chicks.

The chicks will need to be taught to eat and drink. The broody hen will do this naturally, but in her absence you will have to do. Make sure the drinker is already in the unit before introducing the chicks. Introduce each chick individually. Hold its head between your thumb and forefinger with its body in your hand. This will enable you to dip its head into the water in the drinker as you introduce it to its new home. This makes it easier for them to find the water again. They should have a look around their environment after a few minutes and will peck experimentally at the chick crumbs. It usually only takes one to start and the others will follow. If they show no interest in the food at all, take pinches of it and drop it back into the trough. The sound and movement will soon attract their attention and curiosity will take over.

Chicks are attracted to the colour red, which is why most small plastic chick drinkers have a red base. It is best to get a chick trough for the chick crumb, rather than a bowl as the chicks will scratch in a bowl and fling the chick crumb all over the place. Unlike older hens, they will not clear up around the bowl and therefore the food will be wasted. A chick trough has a bar section across the top which prevents the chicks from scratching in it. It also encourages a more orderly feeding time as each chick has a space to itself, rather than a free for all in a bowl.

It is best to raise the drinker and trough off the floor, especially if you are using wood shavings, as the shavings will end up in the drinker base and make it unusable. The same will happen to the trough. If you put the trough and drinker on big enough platforms even the smallest chick can jump up on to it. I use bricks to support the drinker and trough and they work well. The chick needs to be able to jump on the platform, as it will not be able to reach up to a raised drinker if it has to stretch up from the floor.

As the days progress the chicks will need less heat. After the first week their first feathers start to grow on their wings and they become hardier all the time. As this happens they will need less heat, but be guided by them. If they are happy under the lamp leave as it is. If they are all huddled together under it they are cold and there is a

danger of suffocation as they scramble over each other, increase the heat. If they are moving away from the lamp they are too hot, so reduce the heat. Some heat sources come with adjustable heat and the same rule of thumb applies. Find the right heat where the chicks come and go with comfort, not too hot, or too cold or too squashed.

After 4 or 5 weeks the chicks will be very nearly fully feathered and almost ready for the big outside. Now is the time to wean them off the chick crumbs and on to grower pellets. These look exactly the same as layers pellets, so be sure to keep them in distinct containers once they are out of the bag! Start to mix the pellets in with the chick crumbs and reduce the chick crumbs accordingly. The pellets will be left in the trough to begin with, but hunger will get the better of them and they will eventually try them. Sometimes I have had to withdraw the chick crumbs completely and enter into a battle of wills over the pellets as the chicks resolutely refuse to try them. It only takes a day for them to change their minds!

After about 6 weeks, depending on the season, they should be fully feathered and able to have the lamp turned off during the day. They may well have

outgrown the cardboard box, if this is where they were housed in the beginning and will need a bigger compound. I use a dog carrying cage, which works well as the lamp can be fixed quite high up. If it is still cold at night turn the lamp on for them overnight until you are sure they are hardy.

Letting them go outside will depend on the time of year. In the winter months you may have to keep them in longer than in the summer. This means you will have to plan to accommodate your chicks for anything up to 10 weeks. Chicks have terrific throughput and you may find the family complaining about the smell in the downstairs loo after a while, so it is worth giving their accommodation a lot of thought at the outset.

Continue the acclimatisation until they are ready to join the big outdoors. They will be fully developed at around 16 weeks, or when they have grown the last of their tail feathers. At this point they can be transferred on to layers pellets and then wait for those eggs!

Chick Crumbs

Your usual feed supplier will stock chick crumbs, also known as starter ration. Be sure to use crumbs which are in date and check the date if the crumbs are in smaller bags taken from a full bag. If you only have a few chicks you will not need a full 20kg bag, but the smaller bags may have hung around on the shelf, so it is worth checking.

The chick crumb will usually contain coccidiostats, which are an additive to combat coccidiosis, the greatest hazard to chicks. I highly recommend that you ensure that the chick crumb you buy contains coccidiostats to be on the safe side. The only objection would be if you want to raise the chick organically from the outset, in which case a compromise is to fee the chick crumb for a few days when the chick is at its most vulnerable and then switch to an organic compound.

Chick Drinker

When the chicks hatch they are visibly exhausted. Over the next 24 hours they gather strength as they dry and fluff up. When they are transferred to the brooder unit the greatest danger from the drinker is from drowning. For the first few days they are liable so sink to the floor and lay their head down as they rest. If they happen to do that near open water they are liable to lay their heads in the water and drown. If using an open water source, such as a deep saucer, fill it with marbles first so that there is water between the marbles, but not a large enough water surface to drown in.

The best drinker is one designed for chicks. It is similar to a large version, but has a narrow rim to hold the water and minimise the risk of drowning.

Chick Feeder

This is a small trough with a top on it that will allow the chicks' heads in to feed, but stops the chick crumbs from being thrown around. It is also less likely to topple over as the chicks scramble over it.

Heat Lamps

There are three types of heat lamp bulbs: white light, infrared heat and dull emitter. The first two give out heat and either a white or red light. They come in a variety of wattages; 250W, 175W, 100W and 60W. The choice is up to you, or may be limited to what is available. The heat regulation will be made by dimmer switch or height adjustment, so go for the highest wattage available to get the maximum range. The white or red light heat bulbs give off a constant light,

so depending on where the brooder unit is, the chicks may not be able to distinguish between day and night. The dull emitter bulb comes in the same range of wattages, but does not give out any light. A separate light source can be provided if necessary. The dull emitter bulbs are ceramic, rather than glass and about twice the price of the other bulbs, but do last very much longer. If you are going in to rearing seriously they may be worth the investment. Many people feel that the dull emitter bulbs are more natural and therefore better.

There are a range of lamp holders, but they are all based on a metal shade suspended from a cable and chain. Some come with a protective grill over the bulb to prevent any contact with the hot bulb.

If the heat lamp is suspended over the brooder unit the temperature can be varied by raising or lowering the lamp. It the lamp is fixed in the top of an enclosed structure it will benefit from being wired into a dimmer switch, otherwise it will be difficult to lower the temperature as the chicks get older.

13

Children, Chickens & Eggs

Chickens make wonderful pets and there are lots of things to do with eggs besides eating them! This chapter aims to encourage childhood involvement and gives many ideas on creative fun with eggs.

Why did the chicken join the rock band?

(Because she already had the drumsticks!)

Chickens As Pets

Children love collecting the eggs and playing with a tame chicken. I have friends whose daughter takes great delight in taking her favourite chicken for rides in the wheelbarrow.

It is a great start in the responsibility stakes to make it their job to collect the eggs and then to give the hens their evening handfuls of wheat. Neither of these tasks is life threatening for the hens if they are forgotten one day. The next stage of responsibility is bringing the food and water containers in at night, again not life threatening, but running a danger of attracting vermin if forgotten regularly. The third stage of responsibility is letting them out and feeding them in the morning and, finally the ultimate is shutting them in at night. This last one is life threatening if forgotten.

The key is to give your children the level of responsibility they will enjoy and will not cause too much stress in being monitored. The absolute to avoid is the apportionment of any blame if there is a slip up and a fox takes advantage. Unfortunately, it happens.

Hygiene is a consideration and children should be encouraged to wash their hands after handling the hens or collecting the eggs. It works the other way as well and ideally they should wash their hands before collecting the egg to avoid contaminating them!

As well as contributing to the care of the hens children will enjoy working with eggs, from dipping soldiers into lovely yellow yolks to amazing their friends with egg tricks. Here are some easy tricks they will enjoy.

Egg Tricks

Psychic fingers

Tell your friends you have psychic fingers and can feel the difference between a fresh egg and a hard-boiled egg. Prepare for the trick by hard-boiling an egg, preferably one which is the same colour as the fresh egg you are going to use. Ask an adult to help you boil the egg, as it needs to be in boiling water.

To start your trick, pick up one egg and carefully feel the egg with the tips of your fingers. Put that one down and do the same with the other one. This won't tell you which egg is which, but it looks good for the trick. Next spin both eggs on the table top. The one which spins for longer is the hard-boiled one.

How the trick works: The yolk and white are liquid in a fresh egg and move inside when the egg is spun. This makes it wobble, rather than spin properly. The hard-boiled egg always spins smoothly and so spins longer.

The Uncrushable Egg

Amaze your friends with the strength of egg shells. See how many books you can balance on egg shells!

You will need 4 half shells. The remaining shells of eaten hard-boiled eggs will do. Wrap masking tape around the middle and cut the shell so that you have a complete half shell. When you have 4 of these, place them cut side down on the table, book size apart. Carefully place the first book on top and then pile others on top. You'll be amazed at the strength of those little egg shells.

How the trick works: The dome shape of the half shell distributes the weight of the books and gives it extra strength.

The Spooky Floating Egg

Convince a friend you can make an egg rise up out of the water on its own!

173

A fresh egg will sink in water, but with a bit of 'magic' you can make it float up to the top.

You will need: two identical glasses, about 50ml salt and a fresh egg.

Prepare the trick by filling both glasses with water. Then stir the salt into one glass and keep this one hidden.

Ask your friend to put the egg in the water and it will sink. Tell your friend to close their eyes and say 'float' ten times slowly. This will give you enough time to switch the glasses and put the egg in the salt water. Hey presto! The egg is floating!

How the trick works: Salt water is heavier, or denser, than the egg, so making the egg lighter and able to float. If you try different amounts of salt you will be able to make the egg 'hang' in the centre of the glass.

Egg Decoration

It is best not to use fresh eggs for decoration, for obvious reasons, but hard-boiled eggs can be used. If the decorations are to be kept for any length of time it is best to use a blown egg shell.

How To Blow Out a Shell

Wash and dry the egg. Push a big metal needle, such as a tapestry or darning needle, into the pointed end of the shell, to make a small hole. Do the same at the other end, but making a slightly bigger hole and making sure you puncture the yolk. Hold the egg over a bowl and blow through the small hole until the shell is empty. Rinse the shell out and leave to dry thoroughly. The shell is now ready to be decorated.

Tip: The egg contents can be used to make all sorts of dishes, such as omelette, quiche or scrambled eggs.

Egg Yolk Paints

1. Separate the yolk from the white of a fresh egg. Mix 2ml (1/2 tsp.) water with the yolk.

2. Pour a little of the yolk mixture into several small cups. Add food colouring, using a different colour for each cup.

3. Use a brush to paint your egg. If the paint gets too thick, add a few drops of water.

Note: egg yolk paints can be used to paint designs on biscuits before they are put in the oven, or to paint faces or designs on bread before making toast.

Egg Dye

Food colouring, natural colours, and water based-felt pens can be used for colouring eggs. If using food colouring, for each colour, mix 175ml of water and 5ml (1 tsp.) vinegar and 1ml (1/4 tsp.) food colouring to get the right mix. Add the food colouring one drop at a time until you obtain the brightness that you want. Completely submerge the eggs in the mixture, until they are tinted the colour you want, from 2-5 minutes. Remove the eggs from the water and allow to dry before adding another colour or continuing to decorate.

Natural dyes can be made as follows:

Pink

Mix I cup of beetroot water with ½ teaspoon plain vinegar and 3 cups water. Soak cold eggs in the dye for 30 minutes.

Purple

Mix 1 cup purple grape juice, ½ teaspoon vinegar and three cups water. Soak cold eggs in the dye for 30 minutes.

Light Blue

In a pan, mix 1 cup red cabbage leaves, torn and loosely packed, 1 teaspoon vinegar and 3 cups water. Boil mixture for 30 minutes and leave to cool. Strain out the cabbage leaves and soak cold eggs for 30 minutes.

Yellow

As for light blue, but substitute 1 teaspoon turmeric for the cabbage leaves.

An easy way to colour a blown egg is to thread a thin piece of wire through the holes at each end of the egg. Bend the wire at one end so the egg won't slip off. This makes a handy tool for dipping the egg in the dye and hanging it to dry. A cake rack is also useful for drying eggs.

Decoration ideas

First, using an acrylic paint, cover the egg with a uniform or patterned layer of colour and allow it to dry. To stick on a design, use PVA glue to add a small amount of pasta, rice, or beans in the shape of a butterfly, star or letter of the alphabet. Allow the glue to dry for 30 minutes before painting the design.

Use wax crayons, felt pens or paints (acrylics, tempera, enamel or poster paints) on your eggshell. Then coat it with clear nail polish to prevent smearing. To make the eggshell glisten, use pearl-coloured nail polish. Any eggs you wish to keep can be coated with spray lacquer or acrylic sealer.

For egghead faces, use felt pens and paints, or dye eggs flesh colours of brown, pink or yellow.

Glue on ribbons, lace, buttons, cotton balls, wool sequins, macaroni, feathers, glitter, pencil shavings, fabric, yarn, dried plants, buttons, or jewellery.

To make stands for decorated eggs, glue on small plastic curtain rings, buttons, spools, stones, pieces of wood or bottle caps. Strips of coloured heavy paper can be rolled up until small enough to hold an egg and secured with tape.

Egg Shell Mosaic

Recycle broken eggshells to create pretty mosaics. Prepare a variety of dye colours in plastic containers. To dye eggshells quickly, simply immerse them in the food colouring dye mix described on the previous page. The drop of vinegar added to the water will help set the colour. (Leaving the shells in for varied lengths of time will create different shades of colour to work with). Remove shells from dyes and spread them out on paper towels to dry. When the shells are dry, gather the different colours in separate containers.

The shell pieces should be arranged in the basic mosaic design before beginning to glue. When satisfied with the mosaic placement, the shell pieces can be glued into place with PVA glue. If you prefer a shiny glaze on the completed project, use a clear spray lacquer to coat the entire mosaic.

Egg animals

Various animals can be made by using pieces of odds and ends found around the house. Here are some ideas:

Owl

Colour egg with black or brown felt pen. Glue on beak made of triangle construction paper. Use two small stones for feet.

Pig

Dye egg pink. Glue on miniature marshmallows for 4 legs and snout. Make a curly tail from a pipe cleaner. Draw eyes with a felt pen.

Mouse

Dye egg grey. Glue on large pink ovals of construction paper for ears. Add a pipe cleaner tail. Draw on whiskers and eyes with a felt pen.

Bird

Dye egg blue or use a duck egg. Glue on construction paper beak and tissue paper wings and tail. Draw eyes with felt pens

Fish

Dye egg green or colour egg shell green with paint or felt pen. Cut eyes tail and fins from construction paper and glue on.

Marbleised Eggs

Oil and water don't mix, which is what creates many striking designs.

You will need: Egg dye, 1tbsp vegetable oil, and hard-boiled eggs.

Lightly stir the oil into a bowl of egg dye. Immediately dip the egg into the liquid. Or, stand the egg in an eggcup and slowly spoon the mixture over it. When the egg is dry, repeat the process with another colour for an even more interesting effect.

Conclusion

I advised at the beginning of the book to read through it and get a good idea of what Chicken Keeping involves. I very much hope that I have inspired you to keep a few chickens in the knowledge that you will be able to look after them properly. If you already have some hens I hope this book has answered any queries you have looked up in it and helped you find practical solutions to any problems encountered. This is especially with regard to housing. Small annoyances, such as difficulty in getting access to the house to clean it, can soon become big annoyances, but are easily solved with a bit of clever alteration.

Chickens are fun and interesting to have around and your time will be well spent in watching them as they go about their day. Remember the warning though: Chickens are addictive!

With very best wishes for your chicken adventure - Alison Wilson

Alison Wilson has been keeping chickens since 2002. She started with three hens and the magic of that first egg is what inspired her to spread the word and encourage everyone to keep a few hens, just for those fabulous eggs. The fact that they are fabulous pets as well is a bonus! She is a keen photographer and keeps a camera in her farm coat pocket to record events as they happen. She has combined her research, her practical experience and her photographs into this book to help, encourage and inspire you in your new hobby.

Hook Farm Publishing
Hook Farm
London Rd
Hook
RG27 9EQ

www.chickenkeeper.co.uk

Appendix

AGE Wks	AGE Days	VACCINE	ADMINISTRATION	DISEASE	ABBRE.
0 Week	1	RISPENS-THV	INJECT HATCHERY	Marek's Disease Virus / Turkeys Herpes Virus	MDV/ THV
	1	HEALTH CHECK	CHICK PAPERS	Salmonella / Bacterial Viruses	
	5	PARACOX (On Request)	WATER	Coccidiosis	Cocci
1 Week	7	HEALTH CHECK	POST MORTEMS	General Health Check	
	8	GALLIVAC S.e	WATER	Salmonella Enteriditis	SE
2 Weeks	18	D78	WATER	Infectious Bursal Disease / Gumborough Disease	IBD
		H120	WATER	Infectious Bronchitis - M41 Strain	IBD
3 Weeks	21	VITAMINS (Spectrum) - 2 days	WATER	Proactive / Preventative (General Health)	
	25	D78	WATER	Infectious Bursal Disease / Gumborough Disease	IBD
		HB1 NOBLISS	WATER	Newcastle Disease	ND
	26	VITAMINS (Spectrum) - 2 days	WATER	Proactive / Preventative (General Health)	
4 Weeks	28	GALLIVAC S.e	WATER	Salmonella Enteriditis	SE
	32	D78	WATER	Infectious Bursal Disease / Gumborough Disease	IBD
		IB VARIANT	WATER	Infectious Bronchitis - 93B Strain	IBD
5 Weeks	35	Vitamins (Spectrum) - 2 Days	WATER	Proactive / Preventative (General Health)	
7 Weeks	49	ILT	COARSE SPRAY	Infectious Laryngotracheitis	ILT

8 Weeks	60	Ma5 / Clone 30	WATER	Newcastle Disease /1 Bronchitis - M41 Strain	ND/IB
10 Weeks	70	TRT Live (Nemovac)	FINE SPRAY	Turkey Rhino -• Tracheitis	TRT
11 Weeks	80	IB PRIMER (Fort Dodge)	WATER	Infectious Bronchitis - 274 Strain	IB
12 Weeks	84	MANURE TEST FOR WORMS	LITTER	If positive - treat 7 days before depopulation	Worms
13 Weeks	91	IB941	WATER	Infectious Bronchitis - 793B Strain	IB
	93	BLOOD TEST FOR :-		20 Samples from each flock (10 per floor	
		IBM41 IB793B			
		ND MG & MS			
		TRT			
14 Weeks	98	AE	WATER	Avian Encephalomyelitis / Epidemic Tremors	AE/ET
15 Weeks	105	TRT Live (Nemovac)	FINE SPRAY	Turkey Rhino - Tracheitis	TRT
	105	TEST FOR SALMONELLA	Cloacol Swabs	60 Samples from each Flock	SE/ST
			Dust and Environmental	5 different areas	
	105	BLOOD TEST & FREEZE ONLY		20 samples from each flock (10per floor)	
On Delivery		TRIPLE	INJECT	Egg drop Syndrome 1976	EDS '76
				Newcastle Disease	ND
				Infectious Bronchitious	IB
		INACTIVATED TRT (On Request)	INJECT	Turkey Rhino - Tracheitis	TRT

Index

183